Become a top fact-fetcher with CGP!

Quick question — do you own CGP's
Knowledge Organiser for Edexcel GCSE Physics?

You do? Great! Now you can use this Knowledge Retriever
to check you've really remembered all the crucial facts.

There are two memory tests for each topic, plus mixed quiz questions
to make extra sure it's all stuck in your brain. Enjoy.

CGP — still the best! ☺

Our sole aim here at CGP is to produce the highest quality books —
carefully written, immaculately presented and dangerously close to being funny.

Then we work our socks off to get them out to you
— at the cheapest possible prices.

Contents

Published by CGP

From original material by Richard Parsons.

Editors: Josie Gilbert, Sharon Keeley-Holden, Duncan Lindsay, Luke Molloy, Charlotte Sheridan and George Wright.
Contributor: Paddy Gannon.

With thanks to Glenn Rogers for the proofreading.
With thanks to Emily Smith for the copyright research.

ISBN: 978 1 78908 852 6

Printed by Elanders Ltd, Newcastle upon Tyne.
Clipart from Corel®
Illustrations by: Sandy Gardner Artist, email sandy@sandygardner.co.uk

Text, design, layout and original illustrations © Coordination Group Publications Ltd (CGP) 2022
All rights reserved.

How to Use This Book

Every page in this book has a matching page in the GCSE Physics **Knowledge Organiser**.
Before using this book, try to **memorise** everything on a Knowledge Organiser page.
Then follow these **seven steps** to see how much knowledge you're able to retrieve...

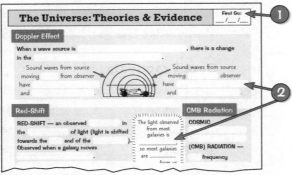

1 In this book, there are two versions of each page. Find the **'First Go'** of the page you've tried to memorise, and write the **date** at the top.

2 Use what you've learned from the Knowledge Organiser to **fill in** any dotted lines or white spaces.

You may need to draw, complete or add labels to diagrams too.

3 Use the Knowledge Organiser to **check your work**.
Use a **different colour pen** to write in anything you missed or that wasn't quite right. This lets you see clearly what you **know** and what you **don't know**.

4 After doing the First Go page, **wait a few days**. This is important because **spacing out** your retrieval practice helps you to remember things better.

5 Now do the **Second Go** page.
The Second Go page is harder — it has more things missing.

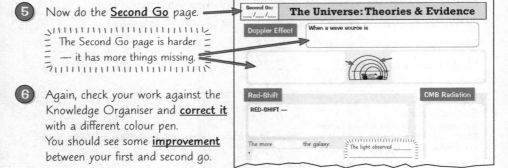

6 Again, check your work against the Knowledge Organiser and **correct it** with a different colour pen.
You should see some **improvement** between your first and second go.

7 **Wait** another few days, then try recreating the whole Knowledge Organiser page on a **blank piece of paper**. If you can do this, you'll know you've **really learned it**.

There are also **Mixed Practice Quizzes** dotted throughout the book:
• The quizzes come in sets of four. They test a mix of content from the previous few pages.
• Do each quiz on a different day — write the date you do each one at the top of the quiz.
• Tick the questions you get right and record your score in the box at the end.

The Scientific Method

Developing Theories

Come up with

↓

↓

Evidence is peer-reviewed

↓

If all evidence backs up
, it becomes
an   .

HYPOTHESIS — a possible

.

PEER REVIEW — when other scientists check results
and explanations before   .

can still change
over time as   is found,
e.g. the theory of   :

Models

REPRESENTATIONAL MODELS — a
, e.g. the kinetic theory

or picture of the

Models help
scientists explain
....
and make
....

COMPUTATIONAL MODELS —   are
used to simulate   .

Issues in Science

Scientific developments can create
four   :

1 Economic — e.g. beneficial   ,
like alternative energy sources, may be
.

2 Environmental — e.g.
could harm the   .

3 Social — decisions based on   can
affect   , e.g.   on fossil fuels.

4 Personal — some decisions affect
, e.g. a person may not want a
wind farm being built
.

Media reports on scientific developments may be
......................., ... or biased.

Hazard and Risk

HAZARD — something that could
potentially   .
RISK — the chance that a
.

Hazards associated with
physics experiments include:

•   from lasers.

• Faulty   equipment.

• Fire from

The seriousness of the
.... and the likelihood
of ....
both need consideration.

The Scientific Method

Developing Theories

Evidence is

If all

HYPOTHESIS —

PEER REVIEW —

can still change over time

e.g.

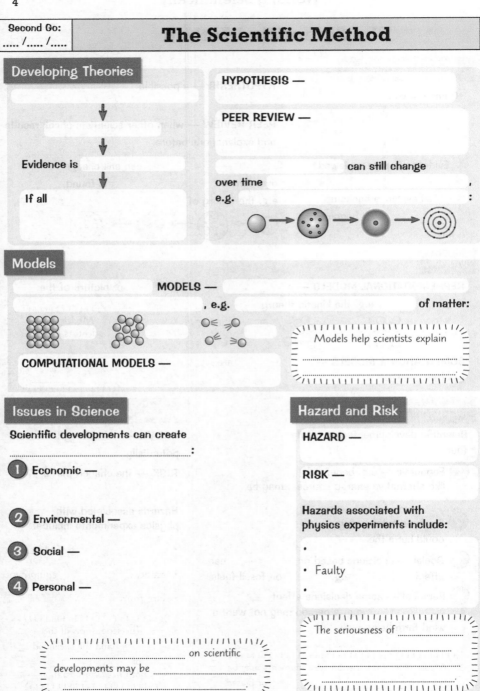

Models

MODELS —

, e.g.

of matter:

COMPUTATIONAL MODELS —

Models help scientists explain

Issues in Science

Scientific developments can create

:

1 Economic —

2 Environmental —

3 Social —

4 Personal —

on scientific developments may be

Hazard and Risk

HAZARD —

RISK —

Hazards associated with physics experiments include:

•

• Faulty

•

The seriousness of

Working Scientifically

Designing & Performing Experiments

Collecting Data

Data should be...

REPEATABLE	gets same results after .... using the .... same .... and ....
REPRODUCIBLE	Similar results can be achieved by .... , or by using a different method or ....
ACCURATE	Results are close to the ....
PRECISE	All data is close to ....

Reliable data is .... and ....

.... results are repeatable and .... and answer the ....

Fair Tests

INDEPENDENT VARIABLE	Variable that you ....
DEPENDENT VARIABLE	Variable that is ....
CONTROL VARIABLE	Variable that is ....
CONTROL EXPERIMENT	An experiment kept under .... as the .... without anything being done to it.
FAIR TEST	An experiment where only .... changes, whilst all other variables are ....

.... are carried out when variables .... be controlled.

Four Things to Look Out For

1. **RANDOM ERRORS** — .... caused by things like .... in measuring.

2. **SYSTEMATIC ERRORS** — measurements that are wrong by ....

3. **ZERO ERRORS** — systematic errors that are caused by using .... that isn't ....

4. **ANOMALOUS RESULTS** — results that .... with the rest of the ....

Processing Data

Calculate the .... — add together all repeat measurements and ....

UNCERTAINTY — the amount by which a .... may differ from the ....

$$\text{uncertainty} = \frac{\quad\quad\quad}{\quad}$$

.... minus

Anomalous results can be .... if you know ....

In any calculation, you should .... the answer to the .... number of .... figures (s.f.) given.

Working Scientifically

6

Designing & Performing Experiments

Collecting Data

Data should be...

REPRODUCIBLE	
	All data

Valid results are

Fair Tests

.... can't be controlled.

DEPENDENT VARIABLE —
CONTROL EXPERIMENT — an experiment kept

Four Things to Look Out For

1 **RANDOM ERRORS —**

2 **SYSTEMATIC ERRORS —**

3 **ZERO ERRORS —**

4 **ANOMALOUS RESULTS —**

Anomalous results ....

Processing Data

— add together

....

UNCERTAINTY —

$$\text{uncertainty} = \frac{}{}$$

In any calculation, ...

Presenting Data

Bar Charts

Bar charts are used when independent variable is _____ or _____ .

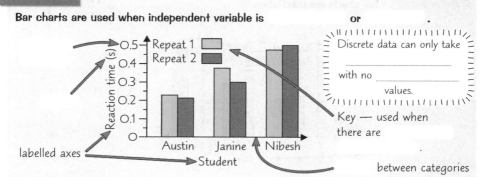

labelled axes

Repeat 1
Repeat 2

Discrete data can only take _____ with no _____ values.

Key — used when there are _____ between categories

Plotting Graphs

Graphs can be used when _____ variables are _____ .

_____ data — can take _____ numerical value within a range.

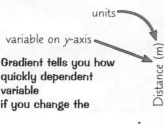

units

_____ variable on y-axis

Gradient tells you how quickly dependent variable _____ if you change the _____ .

gradient = ──────

through (or near to) as many points as possible

points marked with _____ cross

_____ result

_____ scale on axes

_____ variable on x-axis

Three Types of Correlation Between Variables

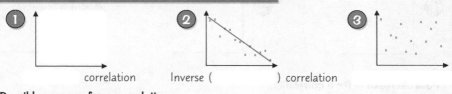

① _____ correlation   ② Inverse (_____) correlation   ③

Possible reasons for a correlation:

Chance — correlation might be _____ .

Third variable — _____ the two variables.

Cause — if every other _____ that could affect the result is _____ , you can conclude that changing one variable _____ .

Working Scientifically

Second Go:
..... /..... /.....

Presenting Data

Bar Charts

Bar charts are used when [_____] .

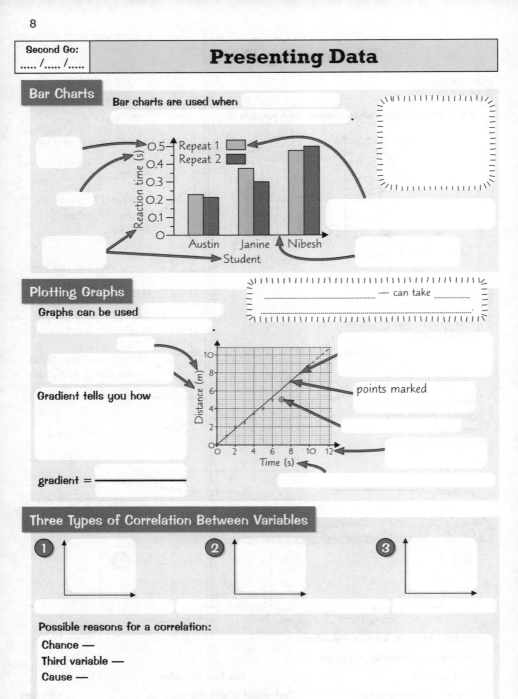

Plotting Graphs

Graphs can be used [_____] .

[_____] — can take [_____]

Gradient tells you how

points marked

gradient = ————————

Three Types of Correlation Between Variables

1   **2**   **3**

Possible reasons for a correlation:

Chance —

Third variable —

Cause —

Conclusions, Evaluations and Units

Conclusions

Draw conclusion by .... between .... variables.

You can only draw a conclusion from ....
.... — you .... go any further than that.

Justify conclusion using ....

Refer to .... and state whether ....

Evaluations

EVALUATION — a .... of the whole investigation.

	Things to consider
Method	• Validity of .... • .... variables
Results	• Reliability, ... , and .... of results • Number of .... • Level of .... in the results
Anomalous results	• Causes of any .... results

You could make ....
based on your conclusion, which you could test ....

Repeating experiment with changes to improve the ....
will give you more .... in your ....

S.I. Units

S.I. BASE UNITS —
a set of ....
that .... use.

Quantity	S.I. Unit
	kilogram ( )
length	( )
	second ( )
temperature	( )
	ampere ( )

Scaling Units

SCALING PREFIX — a word or symbol that goes before .... to indicate a ....

Multiple of unit	Prefix
	tera ( )
10^9	( )
	(M)
1000	( )
	deci ( )
0.01	( )
	(m)
10^{-6}	( )
	nano ( )

 kg ⇄ g

m^3 ⇄ cm^3

Quantities could be in ....
e.g. 1×10^2 m = ... m.

Working Scientifically

Second Go:
..... / ..... / .....

Conclusions, Evaluations and Units

Conclusions

Draw conclusion by

_____

_____ .

Refer to _____ .

You can only draw
a conclusion from
....
.... — you can't
....
....

Evaluations

EVALUATION — _____

_____ .

	Things to consider
Method	•
	•
	•
	•
	•
Anomalous results	•

Repeating experiment

S.I. Units

S.I. BASE UNITS — ....

....
....

Quantity	S.I. Unit
	second (.....)
current	

Scaling Units

SCALING PREFIX —

_____

Multiple of unit	Prefix
	tera (......)
10^{-6}	

kg

Quantities ....
....
....
....
....

Working Scientifically

Mixed Practice Quizzes

Hazard: Quiz questions testing pages 3-10. Risk of doing them: Falling asleep.
Risk of ignoring them: Struggling with science. Conclusion: Give them a try.

Quiz 1   Date: ...... / ...... / ......

1) How do you calculate the range of a set of data?

2) What does it mean if results are valid?

3) Give an example of a personal problem
   that scientific development can cause.

4) State one hazard that is associated with physics experiments.

5) True or false? Accurate results are results that are close to the mean.

6) What is meant by the 'evaluation' of an investigation?

7) What do you have to divide by to get from cm^3 to m^3?

8) State one suitable way to present data
   when the independent variable is discrete.

9) What is an anomalous result?

10) What equation can be used to find the gradient of a graph?

Total:

Quiz 2   Date: ...... / ...... / ......

1) Describe how a hypothesis can become an accepted theory.

2) What is a 'dependent variable'?

3) Give two reasons why a correlation may arise between two variables,
   even if changing one variable doesn't cause the other to change.

4) Give one example of an accepted theory that has changed over time.

5) When can an anomalous result in a data set be ignored?

6) Give the equation used to find the uncertainty for a set of values.

7) State three things that should be considered when evaluating results.

8) True or false? The metre (m) is an S.I. unit used to measure length.

9) Define the term 'peer review'.

10) What is a hazard?

Total:

Mixed Practice Quizzes

Quiz 3   Date: ...... / ...... / ......

1) What is a representational model?
2) Which variable goes on the x-axis of a graph?
3) Describe how to write up a conclusion to an experiment.
4) Define each of the following terms:
   a) Independent variable
   b) Control variable
5) Name two types of experimental error.
6) Which term describes a possible explanation for an observation?
7) What is meant by the term 'uncertainty' when describing data?
8) Which scaling prefix indicates a multiplying factor of 10^6?
9) What does a graph of data with a positive correlation look like?
10) Give one problem associated with media
    reports on scientific developments.

Total:

Quiz 4   Date: ...... / ...... / ......

1) What is: a) repeatable data? b) reproducible data?
2) Give a suitable way to represent data when both variables are continuous.
3) State the S.I. unit for temperature.
4) Give four types of issue that can result from scientific developments.
5) When is a key used in a bar chart?
6) Describe how to calculate the mean of a set of values.
7) True or false? A conclusion cannot go beyond what the data shows.
8) What multiple is nano (n) a prefix for?
9) Give two types of correlation that may be shown by a graph.
10) Give two ways in which models can be useful to scientists.

Total:

Scalars, Vectors and Motion

First Go:
..... /..... /.....

Scalars

SCALAR QUANTITIES —

-
- distance
- mass
-

Vectors

VECTOR QUANTITIES —

- force
-
-
- acceleration
-
- momentum
-

Distance and Displacement

DISTANCE (scalar) — how

(not including its).

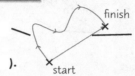
finish
start

(vector) — the and the in a from an object's starting point to its finishing point.

Speed and Velocity

SPEED (scalar) — you're going with .

.... (m) = average speed (..........) × .... (s)

VELOCITY ( ) — speed in a .

Acceleration

ACCELERATION — the in a certain amount of .

(m/s²)

change in velocity ( )
(v is velocity and u is velocity)

= ———— ( )
t——

Acceleration of object close to (object in free fall) is roughly .

Typical Speeds

	Typical speed (m/s)
	1.4
running	3
cycling	
car (built-up area)	13
car (motorway)	
train	up to 55
	250
wind	
	340

Objects, sound and wind rarely travel at a ....

| Second Go: ..... /..... /..... | # Scalars, Vectors and Motion |

Scalars

SCALAR QUANTITIES —

- •
- •

Vectors

VECTOR QUANTITIES —

- force •
- velocity •

Distance and Displacement

DISTANCE ( ) —

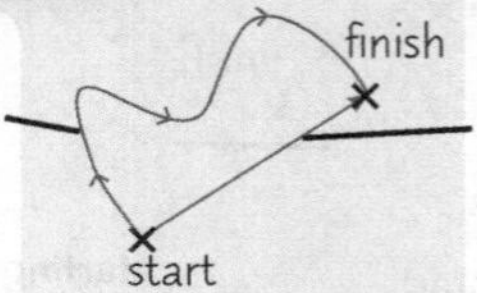

finish

start

DISPLACEMENT ( ) —

Speed and Velocity

SPEED ( ) —

distance travelled (___) =
.... (___) × .... (___)

VELOCITY ( ) —

Acceleration

ACCELERATION —

(m/s²)   change in ( )

(

)

( )

Acceleration of object

Typical Speeds

	Typical speed (m/s)
running	
cycling	
	13
car (motorway)	
	up to 55
	250
wind	

Objects, sound and wind
....
....

Distance/Time and Velocity/Time Graphs

Distance/Time Graphs

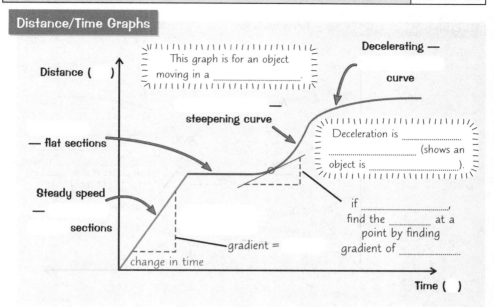

Distance ( )

This graph is for an object moving in a ....

Decelerating — .... curve

— flat sections

steepening curve

Deceleration is .... (shows an object is ....).

Steady speed — .... sections

gradient = ...
change in time

if ...., find the .... at a point by finding gradient of ....

Time ( )

Velocity/Time Graphs

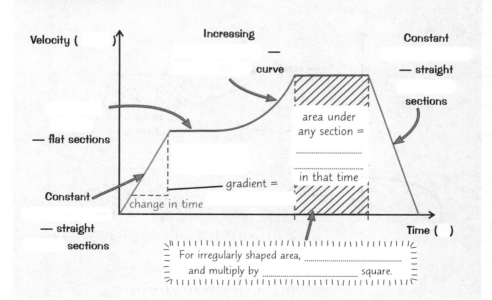

Velocity ( )

Increasing .... curve

Constant .... — straight sections

— flat sections

area under any section = ... in that time

Constant — straight sections

gradient = ...
change in time

For irregularly shaped area, ... and multiply by .... square.

Time ( )

     Section 1 — Motion, Forces and Conservation of Energy

16

Distance/Time and Velocity/Time Graphs

Distance/Time Graphs

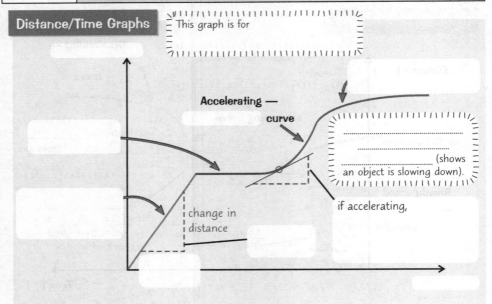

This graph is for

Accelerating — curve

....
.... (shows
an object is slowing down).

change in distance

if accelerating,

Velocity/Time Graphs

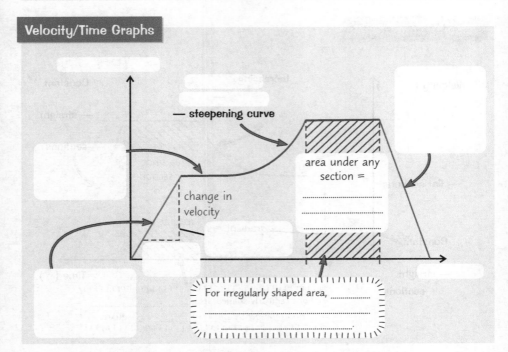

— steepening curve

change in velocity

area under any section =
....
....
....

For irregularly shaped area, ...
....
....

Section 1 — Motion, Forces and Conservation of Energy

Newton's Laws

Newton's First Law

If   resultant force acts on stationary object,   .

If   resultant force acts on moving
object, it   at same
          (same   ).

driving force   resistive force

If   resultant force acts on object,
object   (will change   ,
) in direction of   .

Newton's Second Law

resultant
force (   )
$$F = \frac{mass\ (\quad)}{acceleration\ (\quad)}$$

• Acceleration is
  to   —   .
• Acceleration is inversely proportional to mass.

Newton's Third Law

Two interacting objects exert .... forces on each other.

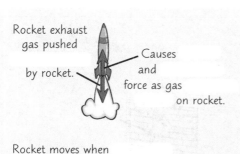
Rocket exhaust
gas pushed
by rocket.
Causes
and
force as gas
on rocket.

Rocket moves when
is greater than   .

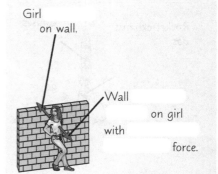
Girl
on wall.

Wall
on girl
with
force.

    Section 1 — Motion, Forces and Conservation of Energy

18

Newton's Laws

Newton's First Law

If [_____] acts on stationary object,
[_____].

force   force

Newton's Second Law

force ( ) [____] **=** [____] mass (kg)

[____]

- **Acceleration is**

- **Acceleration is**

Newton's Third Law

Two interacting objects

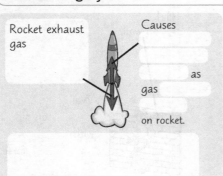

Rocket exhaust gas

Causes [____]

[____] as gas [____]

on rocket.

[____]

[____]

[____]

Section 1 — Motion, Forces and Conservation of Energy

Mixed Practice Quizzes

Time to apply a force on a stationary object and get your brain into motion — these questions test pages 13-18. See if you can improve your score each go.

Quiz 1   Date: ...... / ...... / ......

1) True or false? Vector quantities have magnitude only.

2) What is a typical walking speed?

3) What does the gradient of a velocity-time graph tell you about an object?

4) True or false? The typical speed of sound is 340 m/s.

5) Give two examples of scalar quantities.

6) If a zero resultant force acts on a moving object, does the velocity of the object change or stay the same?

7) What is meant by the velocity of an object?

8) What unit is acceleration measured in?

9) Describe how an object moving along a straight line at a steady speed would be represented on a distance-time graph.

10) True or false? Velocity and speed are vector quantities.

Total:

Quiz 2   Date: ...... / ...... / ......

1) Describe how to find the speed of an object from a distance-time graph.

2) True or false? A stationary object doesn't move when a zero resultant force acts on it.

3) What does a flat section of a velocity-time graph represent?

4) Give the typical speeds for a car in a built-up area and on the motorway.

5) True or false? According to Newton's Second Law, acceleration is inversely proportional to resultant force.

6) Give the definition for acceleration.

7) Is force a scalar or a vector quantity?

8) What is the typical speed for a train?

9) What is Newton's Third Law?

10) What does the gradient of a tangent to a distance-time graph tell you?

Total:

Section 1 — Motion, Forces and Conservation of Energy

Mixed Practice Quizzes

Quiz 3   Date: ...... / ...... / ......

1) What is a typical cycling speed?

2) What is Newton's First Law?

3) True or false? The acceleration of an object due to gravity close to the Earth's surface is roughly 12.8 m/s².

4) Give the equation that links average speed, distance travelled and time.

5) Describe the difference between scalar and vector quantities.

6) What does the gradient of a distance-time graph tell you about an object?

7) True or false? If you apply a force to an object, the object pushes back with a smaller force.

8) Describe how an object with a constant deceleration would be represented on a velocity-time graph.

9) Is distance a scalar or a vector quantity?

10) Give the equation for calculating acceleration, defining each symbol used.

Total:

Quiz 4   Date: ...... / ...... / ......

1) True or false? Scalar quantities have a magnitude and a direction.

2) True or false? The velocity of an object will only change if a non-zero resultant force acts on the object.

3) What does a flat section of a distance-time graph represent?

4) What is a typical running speed?

5) What does the area under a section of a velocity-time graph tell you?

6) Describe how the speed of an object is changing when it is decelerating.

7) Give three examples of vector quantities.

8) Give the equation for Newton's Second Law, defining each term used and their units.

9) Describe how an object accelerating along a straight line would be represented on a distance-time graph.

10) What unit is speed measured in?

Total:

Section 1 — Motion, Forces and Conservation of Energy

Weight, Mass and Circular Motion

Weight, Mass and Gravity

WEIGHT — .... that acts
on an object due to ....

weight ( )

$$W = mg$$

Near Earth, weight is
caused by

Measure weight
with ....
....
....

The ....
.... is the
point at which an
object's ....
.... to act.

- Object weight depends on .... of
  .... at object location.
- .... has .... value anywhere in the Universe.

Mass and Motion

INERTIAL MASS — measure of
.... it is to change an object's
.... It's the .... of force over
acceleration: ....

Same .... applied to
bowling ball and golf ball.

.... acceleration

.... acceleration

Bowling ball has bigger .... ,
so it's harder to .... its ....

Circular Motion

Object in circular motion with
constant speed is always
.... ,
so object has ....
....

Changing .... means object
is .... , so there is a
.... on it.

This force is the
.... It always acts towards
....

Weight, Mass and Circular Motion

Weight, Mass and Gravity

WEIGHT —

Measure

$W =$

mass (kg)

Near Earth,

- **Object weight**

- **Object mass**

Mass and Motion

INERTIAL MASS —

Same
bowling ball and golf ball.

$F \longrightarrow$

$F \longrightarrow$

Bowling ball has

Circular Motion

Object in circular motion

Changing velocity means

This force is

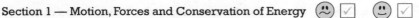

Momentum

Calculating Momentum

momentum ( )

$$p = mv$$ (m/s)

- The greater _____,
  the greater its momentum.

- The greater
  _____, the greater its
  momentum.

Conservation of Momentum

CONSERVATION OF MOMENTUM —

in a _____, total momentum
_____ (e.g. a _____)
equals total momentum _____ an event.

_____ explosion,
momentum is _____.

_____ explosion, pieces fly off in
different directions so momentum _____.

Newton's Third Law and Momentum

For two balls of the same _____ :

Ball A approaches with _____ p
and _____ with Ball B.

 $p =$

Ball A and Ball B exert _____
on each other due to _____.

Due to _____, Ball A _____ at
the same rate that Ball B _____.

The _____ the force is applied is the _____ for both
balls, so their _____.

$= v_B$

Momentum lost by Ball A equals
_____. So total momentum _____
before equals _____.

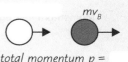
total momentum $p =$

Momentum

Calculating Momentum

$$p = \boxed{}$$

mass (kg)

-

-

Conservation of Momentum

CONSERVATION OF MOMENTUM —

Before explosion,

After explosion,

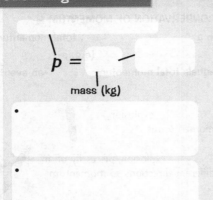

Newton's Third Law and Momentum

For two balls of the [   ] :

Ball A approaches

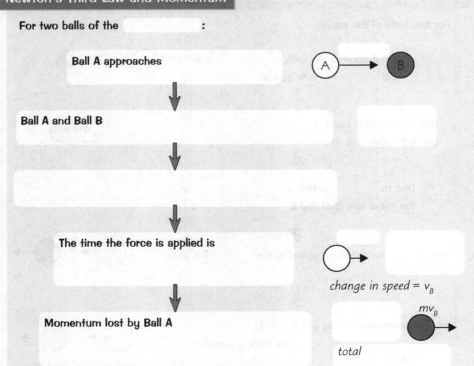

Ball A and Ball B

The time the force is applied is

change in speed = v_B

Momentum lost by Ball A

mv_B

total

Section 1 — Motion, Forces and Conservation of Energy ☑ ☑ ☑

Reaction Times and Stopping Distances

Reaction Times

Typical human reaction time:

Three factors affecting reaction times:

 1

 2 Drugs and alcohol

3

Three Steps to do the Ruler Drop Test

1 Get someone to hold ruler so

2 Ruler dropped

3 Use distance ruler fell

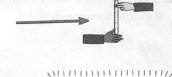

distance fallen

The longer the distance, ...

Stopping Distance Equation

Distance taken to stop

Stopping distance = ... distance + ... distance

How far vehicle moves during ....
....

Two factors that increase thinking distance:

1 faster vehicle

2 long driver

Four factors that increase braking distance:

1 faster vehicle speed

2

3 .... road surface

4 damaged or worn

If .... doubles, thinking distance .... and braking distance ....

Work Done When Stopping

For car to stop,
by brakes equals energy in car's
....

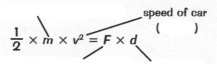

$$\frac{1}{2} \times m \times v^2 = F \times d$$

speed of car
( )

distance
( )

A good estimate for a car's mass ....

Large Decelerations

The .... a vehicle is going, the
.... needed
to make it stop in a ....

Larger
means larger ....

Very large .... can cause:
• brakes to
• vehicle to

Second Go: ...../...../..... Reaction Times and Stopping Distances

Reaction Times   Typical

Three factors affecting reaction times:

1. _____
2. _____
3. _____

Three Steps to do the Ruler Drop Test

1. Get someone to _____

2. _____

3. Use distance _____

Stopping Distance Equation

Distance taken to _____

_____ = _____ distance + _____ distance

How far _____

Two factors that increase thinking distance:

1. _____
2. _____

Four factors that increase braking distance:

1. _____
2. _____
3. _____
4. _____

If _____, thinking distance _____ and braking distance _____.

Work Done When Stopping

For car to stop, _____

_____ of car (kg)   _____ of car (____)

_____ = F

_____ (m)

Large Decelerations

The faster a vehicle is going, the greater the _____

_____

_____ can cause:

• _____   • _____

Section 1 — Motion, Forces and Conservation of Energy

Mixed Practice Quizzes

Pages 21-26 are tested in these next quizzes. Give them a go and get the weight off your shoulders. Remember to add up your scores after you're done.

Quiz 1
Date: ...... / ...... / ......

1) What is meant by conservation of momentum?

2) What does a calibrated spring-balance measure?

3) What is inertial mass?

4) True or false? The slower a car is travelling,
the more work done by the brakes bringing it to a stop.

5) Give a typical human reaction time.

6) Give two negative effects caused by the large deceleration of a vehicle.

7) What is the name for the force that acts on an object due to gravity?

8) Give the formula for calculating momentum.

9) True or false? Distractions can affect your ability to react.

10) Apart from its mass, what does the weight of an object depend on?

Total:

Quiz 2
Date: ...... / ...... / ......

1) Name four factors that increase the braking distance of a vehicle.

2) True or false? Objects in circular motion experience a resultant force.

3) The stopping distance of a vehicle is the sum of
the thinking distance and what other distance?

4) True or false? When two objects collide, both objects exert forces.

5) Two objects are travelling at the same velocity. One has a larger mass and
the other has a smaller mass. Which object will have a larger momentum?

6) True or false? The greater the speed of a vehicle,
the greater its stopping distance.

7) Name three factors that affect reaction times.

8) What are the units of momentum?

9) If a person with a long reaction time does the ruler drop test,
will the ruler fall a short way or a long way before they catch it?

10) If a vehicle's speed doubles, does the thinking distance double or halve?

Total:

Mixed Practice Quizzes

Quiz 3   Date: ...... / ...... / ......

1) Why would longer reaction times increase the stopping distance of a car?

2) Give the equation for calculating the weight of an object, defining each symbol used.

3) Explain why an object moving in a circular motion with a constant speed has a changing velocity.

4) True or false? Weight has the units N/kg.

5) True or false? A larger braking force means a larger deceleration.

6) Describe an experiment you could do to investigate someone's reaction time.

7) What is meant by the braking distance of a vehicle?

8) If the same force is applied to two objects, how does their inertial mass affect their acceleration?

9) The momentum of an object depends on mass and what other variable?

10) Give two factors that increase thinking distance.

Total:

Quiz 4   Date: ...... / ...... / ......

1) What is gravitational field strength measured in?

2) Why can large decelerations be dangerous?

3) True or false? When two objects collide, their total momentum decreases.

4) Name one other factor, apart from tiredness, that can affect reaction time.

5) What is meant by the thinking distance?

6) What does the work done by a car's brakes need to equal to bring the car to a stop?

7) Name a piece of apparatus that can be used to measure weight.

8) In circular motion, what is the force that acts towards the centre of the circle called?

9) True or false? If a vehicle's speed doubles, its braking distance quadruples.

10) Define inertial mass as a ratio.

Total:

Energy Stores and Transfers

Eight Types of Energy Store

1.
2.   potential
3.   potential
4. Electrostatic
5.
6. Chemical
7. Magnetic
8.

Four Types of Energy Transfer

1.   (a force doing work)
2. Electrical (
)
3.
4. Radiation
   (e.g.   )

Kinetic Energy

kinetic energy (   )

$$KE = \frac{1}{2}m\quad^2$$

(kg)   speed (   )

Gravitational Potential Energy

change in
vertical
height (m)

(kg)

$$\triangle GPE = mg\triangle h$$

(J)

gravitational   (N/kg)

Systems and Conservation of Energy

SYSTEM —   .

CONSERVATION OF ENERGY — energy can be   ,
        or   but not   or   .

CLOSED SYSTEM — no   is transferred
        , so there is   in total energy.

Pan and hob = **NOT** a   .
Energy is transferred   .

Energy
(by heating)

Some
as energy transferred to

increasing its

of surroundings.

     Section 1 — Motion, Forces and Conservation of Energy

Energy Stores and Transfers

Eight Types of Energy Store

1
2
3
4
5   7
6   8

Four Types of Energy Transfer

1
2
3
4

Kinetic Energy

$$KE = \frac{1}{2}mv^2$$

Gravitational Potential Energy

change in

$$\triangle GPE =$$

Systems and Conservation of Energy

SYSTEM —

CONSERVATION OF ENERGY —

CLOSED SYSTEM —

Pan and hob =   .
Energy is   .

Energy

Some energy

Energy Transfers

Energy Transfer Diagrams for Six Different Systems

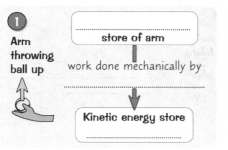

1 Arm throwing ball up

....
store of arm

work done mechanically by
....

Kinetic energy store
....

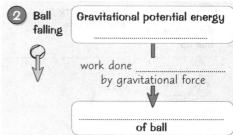

2 Ball falling

Gravitational potential energy
....

work done .... by gravitational force

....
of ball

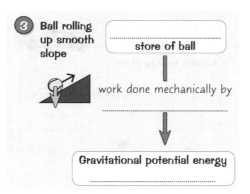

3 Ball rolling up smooth slope

....
store of ball

work done mechanically by
....

Gravitational potential energy
....

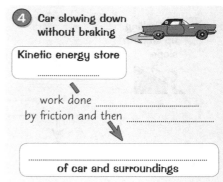

4 Car slowing down without braking

Kinetic energy store
....

work done .... by friction and then ....

....
of car and surroundings

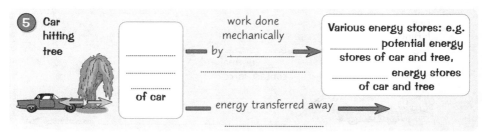

5 Car hitting tree

....
....
....
of car

work done mechanically — by ....

Various energy stores: e.g. .... potential energy stores of car and tree, ... energy stores of car and tree

energy transferred away ⟶
....

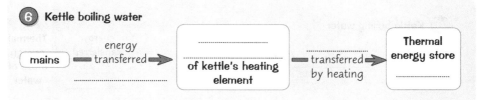

6 Kettle boiling water

mains — energy transferred⟶
....

....
of kettle's heating element

— transferred⟶ by heating

Thermal energy store
....

    Section 1 — Motion, Forces and Conservation of Energy

Energy Transfers

Energy Transfer Diagrams for Six Different Systems

1 Arm throwing ball up

Chemical energy store of arm

....

....

....

2 Ball falling

3 Ball rolling up smooth slope

4 Car slowing down without braking

Kinetic energy store

....

....

5 Car hitting tree

.... normal contact force

....

6 Kettle boiling water

.... energy transferred

Thermal energy store of water

....

....

Section 1 — Motion, Forces and Conservation of Energy

Efficiency and Reducing Energy Loss

Efficiency Equation

Efficiency = $\dfrac{\text{transferred}}{\text{Total energy}}$

No device is   efficient.

In all systems, energy is
(wasted) to a store that's
(usually thermal).

If a mechanical process causes a rise in
temperature, energy is
heating

Efficiency in Diagrams

Arrow widths proportional
to   .

E.g.

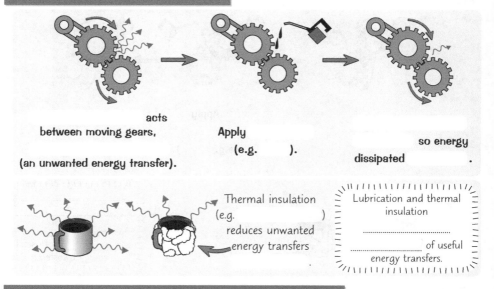

total

} energy transfers

energy transfer

Lubrication and Thermal Insulation

acts
between moving gears,   **Apply**
(e.g.   ).

(an unwanted energy transfer).

so energy
dissipated

Thermal insulation
(e.g.   )
reduces unwanted
energy transfers

Lubrication and thermal
insulation
....
.... of useful
energy transfers.

Two Ways to Decrease How Quickly a Building Cools

1. Increase   of its   .

2. Make walls out of material with
   .

The higher a material's
.....................................,'
the .... it transfers
energy by ....

CONDUCTION — where   particles
transfer   to   .

Second Go: ...../...../..... Efficiency and Reducing Energy Loss

Efficiency Equation

Efficiency = _____

> **No device**
> **In all systems,**
>
> **If a mechanical process**

Efficiency in Diagrams

_____ proportional to

_____

E.g.

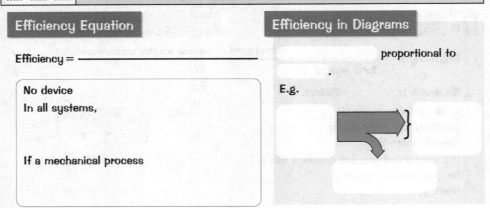

Lubrication and Thermal Insulation

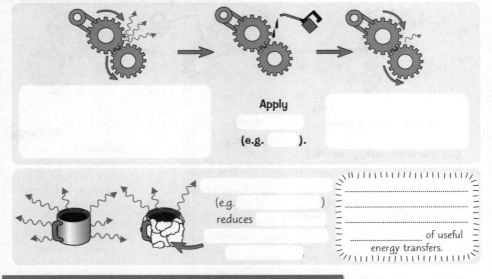

Apply

(e.g.   ).

(e.g.   )
reduces

_____

_____ of useful
energy transfers.

Two Ways to Decrease How Quickly a Building Cools

1

2 **Make walls**

CONDUCTION —

The higher

Section 1 — Motion, Forces and Conservation of Energy

Energy Resources

Non-Renewable and Renewable Energy Resources

NON-RENEWABLE ENERGY RESOURCES — energy resources that will

.

RENEWABLE ENERGY RESOURCES — energy resources that will

.

Three Fossil Fuels [Non-renewable]

1 Coal   **2** Oil — Used to make
(
) for cars.

3 (Natural) Gas — Used to
homes and
.

All three fossil fuels are   to generate   .

- Burning fossil fuels   , contributing to   .
- Burning coal and oil releases   , causing   .

Tidal Power [ ]

Tide comes in.

Water builds

Water

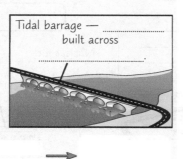

Tidal barrage — ....
built across
.... :

- Produce   when in use.
- Disturb habitats of
and   .

Nuclear Power

[Non-renewable]

Nuclear fuel

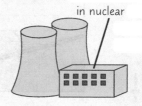

in nuclear

,

- Nuclear waste is
to
.
- Carries the risk of a
.

Energy Resources

Non-Renewable and Renewable Energy Resources

NON-RENEWABLE ENERGY RESOURCES —

RENEWABLE ENERGY RESOURCES —

Three Fossil Fuels

 Coal   Oil

Used to

3 (Natural) Gas

Used to

All three fossil fuels are

• Burning

• Burning

Tidal Power

Tide comes in.

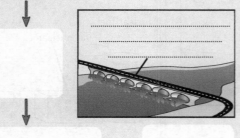

Nuclear Power

Nuclear fuel

•

•

•
•

Energy Resources and Trends in Use

Solar Power

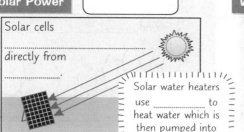

Solar cells

....

directly from

....

Solar water heaters use .... to heat water which is then pumped into

....

• Produce ....
  when in use.

Wind Power — Renewable

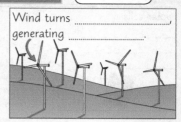

Wind turns ....,
generating ....

• Produce .... when in use.

• .... and ....

Bio-fuels

Made from

or ....

Bio-fuels are burned to

.... , and

used as ....

• In some regions, ... destroyed to ...., so species lose ....

Hydro-electric Power — Renewable

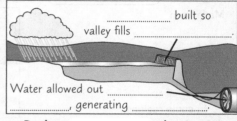

.... built so valley fills ....

Water allowed out ...., generating ....

• Produce .... when in use.

• Flooding valley has big impact on .... and can cause ....

Trends in Energy Use

1900–2000

Electricity use increased as:

• ....

• people began to use ....

2000 onwards

Electricity use decreasing as:

• appliances are ....

• people are .... with amount of ....

Three reasons we're increasing use of renewables:

1. .... is very damaging to environment.

2. We need to .... without .... before they run out.

3. Pressure on .... and .... has led them to ....

Changing to renewables is limited by their .... and ....

   Section 1 — Motion, Forces and Conservation of Energy

Second Go:
...../...../......

Energy Resources and Trends in Use

Solar Power

Solar cells

....

use the sun to ....

....

....

•

Wind Power

Wind ....

....

•

•

Bio-fuels

Made from

Bio-fuels

• **In some regions,**

Hydro-electric Power

....

Water

....

•

• **Flooding valley**

Trends in Energy Use

1900–2000

Electricity use .... as:

•

•

2000 onwards

Electricity use .... as:

•

•

Three reasons we're increasing use of renewables:

1

2

3

Changing to renewables is ....

Mixed Practice Quizzes

If you think doing quizzes based on stuff from pages 29-38 sounds like a bad idea, don't look down. Oh no, you looked. That means you have to do them now.

Quiz 1   Date: ...... / ...... / ......

1) State two energy resources that are burned to generate electricity. ☑

2) In what type of system is there no net change in the total energy in the system when energy is transferred? ☐

3) Would a building cool quicker with thinner or thicker walls? ☐

4) Give one reason why electricity use increased from 1900 to 2000. ☐

5) Describe how energy is transferred when a car hits a tree. ☑

6) True or false? In some systems, energy is never dissipated. ☐

7) How is electricity generated by a tidal barrage? ☑

8) True or false? Energy is transferred mechanically when a force does work. ☐

9) What are bio-fuels made from? ☐

10) Name an energy resource that doesn't produce pollution when in use. ☐

Total: ☐

Quiz 2   Date: ...... / ...... / ......

1) True or false? Energy can be transferred usefully, created and destroyed. ☐

2) Which one of the following is a non-renewable energy resource?
   A. Wind power   B. Bio-fuels   C. Tidal power   D. Nuclear power ☑

3) Describe how energy is transferred when a kettle boils water. ☐

4) What is meant by a closed system? ☐

5) State two environmental impacts of burning fossil fuels. ☐

6) Give two reasons why the use of renewable energy resources is increasing. ☑

7) What equation can be used to find the amount of energy in an object's kinetic energy store? ☑

8) Name three renewable energy resources. ☐

9) State two ways that energy can be transferred between stores. ☑

10) True or false? Thermal insulation can increase the efficiency of useful energy transfers. ☑

Total: ☐

Mixed Practice Quizzes

Quiz 3

Date: ...... / ...... / ......

1) How can you reduce the energy dissipated in energy transfers between moving parts?

2) Name three types of fossil fuel.

3) State two negative impacts tidal barrages can have on the environment.

4) Does thermal insulation increase or decrease unwanted energy transfers?

5) What equation can be used to find the change in the amount of energy in an object's gravitational potential energy store?

6) True or false? The higher a material's thermal conductivity, the faster it transfers energy by conduction.

7) What type of energy store is dissipated energy usually transferred to?

8) What is meant by a renewable energy resource?

9) True or false? Energy can be transferred by heating.

10) Describe how energy is transferred when a ball rolls up a slope.

Total:

Quiz 4

Date: ...... / ...... / ......

1) True or false? If a mechanical process causes a rise in temperature, energy is dissipated.

2) What device generates electricity directly from sunlight?

3) What is meant by the conservation of energy?

4) Give an equation that can be used to calculate efficiency.

5) True or false? Lubrication reduces the energy dissipated by moving parts by reducing the friction between them.

6) State two reasons why changing to renewable resources is limited.

7) The amount of energy in an object's kinetic energy store depends on its speed and what other property?

8) Describe one potential environmental impact of using nuclear power.

9) Describe the changes in the way energy is stored when:
   a) a ball is thrown upwards   b) a ball falls under gravity

10) Name three types of energy stores.

Total:

Wave Basics

Wave Properties

When waves travel through a medium, they _____ (but not _____).

Sound waves move away...
...the _____
_____.

Ripples on water's surface move away...
...the _____
_____.

FREQUENCY — number of _____ of the wave passing a certain point _____.

AMPLITUDE — _____ of a point on a wave from _____

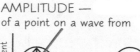

PERIOD — amount of _____ it takes for one _____ of a wave.

period = 1 ÷ _____

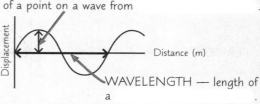

WAVELENGTH — length of a _____.

Transverse Waves

Vibrations _____ to direction _____ (at 90°).

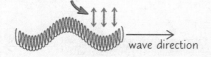
wave direction

Three types of transverse waves:

1 _____ in water

2 Electromagnetic waves (e.g. _____)

3 _____-waves

Longitudinal Waves

Vibrations _____ to direction wave travels.

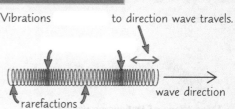
rarefactions
wave direction

Two types of longitudinal waves:

1 _____ waves

2 _____-waves

Wave Speed

Wave _____ is the wave's speed _____.

WAVE SPEED — how _____ a wave _____.

$$v = \frac{distance\ (\ )}{t\ time\ (s)}$$
(   )

$$v = \lambda \times frequency\ (\quad,\ Hz)$$
(   )   (m)

       Section 2 — Waves and the Electromagnetic Spectrum

Wave Basics

Wave Properties

When waves travel through a

Sound waves

...the

Ripples

...

...the

FREQUENCY —

PERIOD — amount of

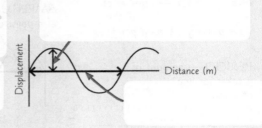

Displacement

Distance (m)

period = ...

Transverse Waves

Vibrations

wave

Three types of transverse waves:

1

2

3

Longitudinal Waves

Vibrations

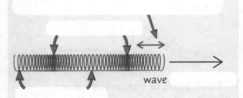

wave

Two types of longitudinal waves:

1

2

Wave Speed

WAVE SPEED —

$v = \dfrac{}{}$ (m)

$v =$ (, Hz)

wavelength (   )

Wave Behaviour at Boundaries

Boundaries

When a wave hits a   ,
it can be...

→ absorbed

⇄

→ or transmitted:
→ not refracted

What happens
depends on
....
of wave and
....
of ....

Reflection

The normal is a line
.... to
surface at point of ....

incoming ray   ray
angle of   angle of

boundary

LAW OF   —
Angle of incidence =   .

Refraction

.... never changes during refraction.

REFRACTION — when a wave .... as it
crosses a .... between two materials at an .... to the ....

Wave ⟨ slows down → Wavelength   . → Bends   normal.
       speeds up → Wavelength   . → Bends   normal.

Typically, ... waves slow down in
.... materials, and speed up
in .... materials.

WAVEFRONT — an .... that
represents the .... on each wave.

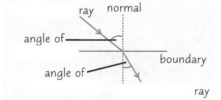

ray normal

angle of

angle of

boundary

ray

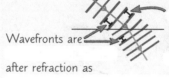

Wavefronts are   between two
                        wavefronts =

after refraction as

Total Internal Reflection

TOTAL .... REFLECTION — when ....
light incident on a boundary is ....

.... **ANGLE —** the .... angle
at which total internal reflection occurs.

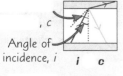

, c

Angle of
incidence, i   i   c

refracted,
some

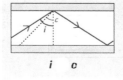

i   c

reflection

Diffuse Reflection

Rays reflected in

Rough surfaces (e.g.   )
appear   .

Specular Reflection

Rays reflected in

surfaces (e.g.
) give   reflection.

      Section 2 — Waves and the Electromagnetic Spectrum

44

Wave Behaviour at Boundaries

Boundaries

When a _____,
it can be...

reflected

or

refracted

What happens
depends on
....
....
....

Reflection

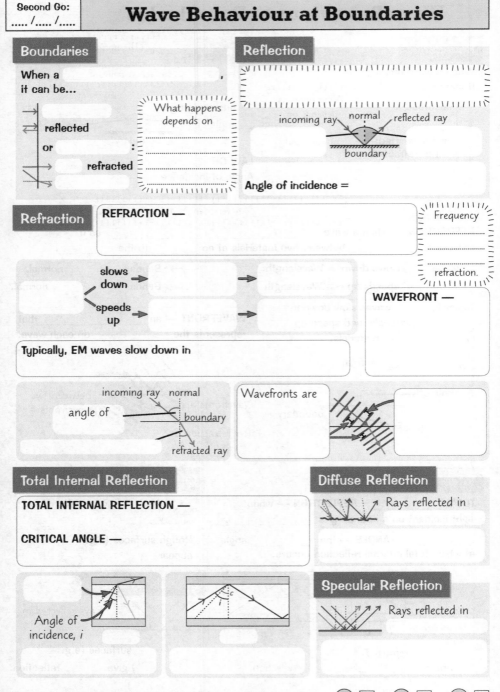

incoming ray   normal   reflected ray

boundary

Angle of incidence =

Refraction

REFRACTION —

Frequency
....
....
....
refraction.

slows
down →

speeds
up →

WAVEFRONT —

Typically, EM waves slow down in

incoming ray   normal

angle of

boundary

refracted ray

Wavefronts are

Total Internal Reflection

TOTAL INTERNAL REFLECTION —

CRITICAL ANGLE —

Angle of
incidence, i

Diffuse Reflection

Rays reflected in

Specular Reflection

Rays reflected in

Section 2 — Waves and the Electromagnetic Spectrum

Sound

Vibrations

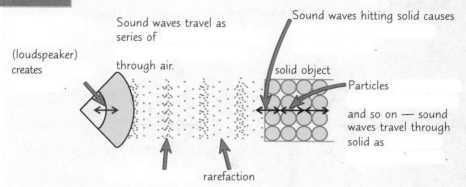

Sound waves travel as series of

(loudspeaker) creates

through air.

Sound waves hitting solid causes

solid object

Particles

and so on — sound waves travel through solid as

rarefaction

When a wave enters a medium and speeds up:

- wavelength
- frequency

Hearing Sound

Sound waves   .

Cause eardrum   .

These   cause other parts of ear to   , allowing you to   .

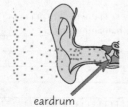

eardrum

Limited Frequency Range

Conversion of sound waves to   in a   object only occurs over a certain   .

Three factors that

are the   object's:

①
②
③

E.g. in human hearing, conversion of sound to .... is limited by .... and .... of eardrum, and structure of ....

    Section 2 — Waves and the Electromagnetic Spectrum

Second Go:
..... /..... /.....

Sound

Vibrations

Sound waves travel

Sound waves

solid object

Particles hit

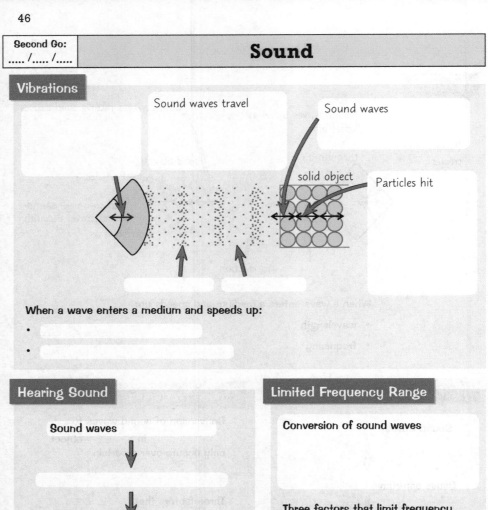

When a wave enters a medium and speeds up:

-
-

Hearing Sound

Sound waves

⬇

These vibrations

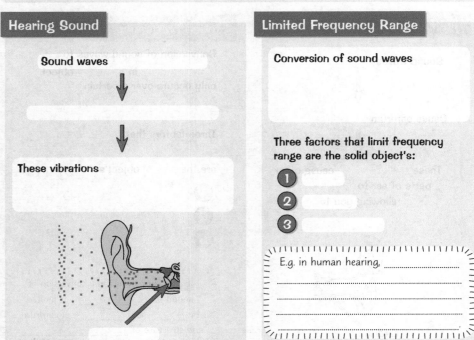

Limited Frequency Range

Conversion of sound waves

Three factors that limit frequency range are the solid object's:

1.
2.
3.

E.g. in human hearing, ...
....
....
....

Ultrasound, Infrasound & Seismic Waves

Ultrasound

ULTRASOUND — sound waves with frequencies _____ .

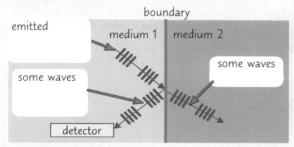

boundary

emitted _____

medium 1 | medium 2

some waves _____

some waves _____

detector

**Time it takes
ultrasound waves to be _____

_____ from boundary and
_____ can be
used to measure _____** .

Two uses of ultrasound:

1 Medical imaging, e.g. _____ .

2 _____ (sonar),
e.g. finding _____ of water or
_____ in deep water.

To find _____ to sea floor/object,
_____ for
ultrasound to travel there and back.
Use this _____ along with
_____ in $x = vt$.

Seismic Waves

INFRASOUND — sound waves with
_____ lower than _____ .

_____ produce _____ at
a range of frequencies — including _____ .
Detecting _____ gives
for _____ of Earth's core and _____ :

Scientists can _____
to predict _____ e.g. volcanoes.

outer core

(almost) solid

P-waves
• _____ waves.
• Travel through _____ .

S-waves
• _____ waves.
• Can't travel through _____ .

P-waves pass _____
and _____
_____ are _____ .

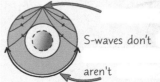

S-waves don't _____
and _____
_____ aren't _____ .

      Section 2 — Waves and the Electromagnetic Spectrum

Second Go:
...../...../.....

Ultrasound, Infrasound & Seismic Waves

Ultrasound

ULTRASOUND —

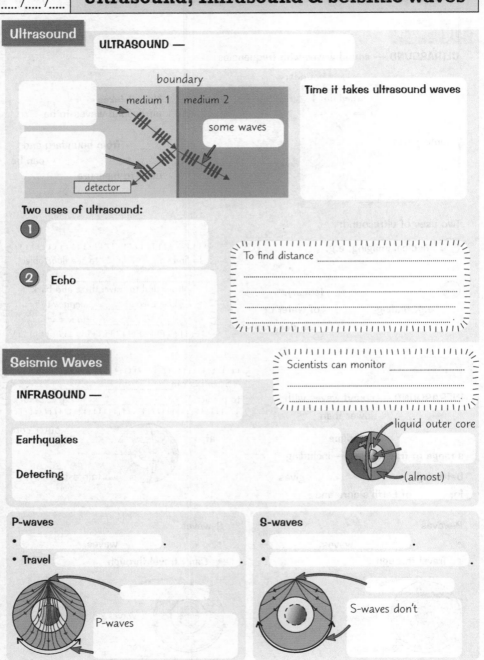

boundary

medium 1 | medium 2

some waves

detector

Time it takes ultrasound waves

Two uses of ultrasound:

①

② Echo

To find distance ....
....
....
....

Seismic Waves

Scientists can monitor ....
....
....

INFRASOUND —

Earthquakes

Detecting

liquid outer core

(almost)

P-waves

•

• Travel

P-waves

S-waves

•

•

S-waves don't

Section 2 — Waves and the Electromagnetic Spectrum

Mixed Practice Quizzes

Time to reflect on what you've learnt so far by doing some questions covering
p.41-48. Tick off each question you get right to keep track of your progress.

Quiz 1   Date: ...... / ...... / ......

1) Describe the difference between transverse and longitudinal waves.

2) Why can humans only hear a limited frequency range of sound waves?

3) True or false? Ripples on a water's surface carry the water away.

4) If a wave refracts and slows down,
   what happens to its wavelength and direction?

5) True or false? If a sound wave enters a medium
   and speeds up, its frequency increases.

6) State one use of detecting P-waves and S-waves.

7) A wave can be reflected when it hits a boundary.
   State two other things that can happen to a wave when it hits a boundary.

8) What is meant by total internal reflection?

9) Are electromagnetic waves transverse or longitudinal?

10) Define wave speed.

Total:

Quiz 2   Date: ...... / ...... / ......

1) Define: a) the 'period' of a wave, b) the 'frequency' of a wave.

2) What can echo sounding (sonar) be used for?

3) What happens to the particles in a solid when a sound wave hits the solid?

4) Give one use of infrasound.

5) What type of surface reflects light rays in all directions?

6) True or false? The angle of incidence always equals the
   angle of reflection when a ray is reflected at a boundary.

7) True or false? Transverse waves have compressions and rarefactions.

8) What are the units of frequency?

9) A wave refracts at a boundary and speeds up.
   State how its wavelength changes.

10) What equation links wave speed, distance and time?

Total:

Mixed Practice Quizzes

Quiz 3   Date: ...... / ...... / ......

1) How can ultrasound waves be used to find the distance to the sea floor?

2) What is a wavefront?

3) Give one example of a transverse wave and one example of a longitudinal wave.

4) What is infrasound?

5) What does the ray diagram look like for the refraction of a wave that decreases in speed as it hits a boundary?

6) True or false? Waves transfer energy and matter.

7) Describe how sound waves travel through a solid.

8) True or false? Light will be totally internally reflected if its angle of incidence is greater than the critical angle.

9) Define: a) the 'amplitude' of a wave, b) the 'wavelength' of a wave.

10) When sound waves reach your ear, what enables you to hear sound?

Total:

Quiz 4   Date: ...... / ...... / ......

1) Describe the difference between diffuse reflection and specular reflection.

2) What equation links wave speed, frequency and wavelength?

3) Give two factors that limit the frequency range of sound waves a solid can transmit.

4) Is it transverse waves or longitudinal waves that have vibrations perpendicular to the direction the wave travels?

5) What is the name for sound waves with frequencies higher than 20 kHz?

6) True or false? The eardrum vibrates when sound waves hit it.

7) What is refraction?

8) If a sound wave enters a medium and its wavelength increases, what happens to its frequency and wave speed?

9) Ultrasound can be used for medical imaging. What else can ultrasound be used for?

10) True or false? The distance between two wavefronts is the amplitude.

Total:

Colour

Colour and Wavelength

In the   spectrum, every   has a small range of   .

←——————————— decreasing   ——————————→

orange   green   indigo

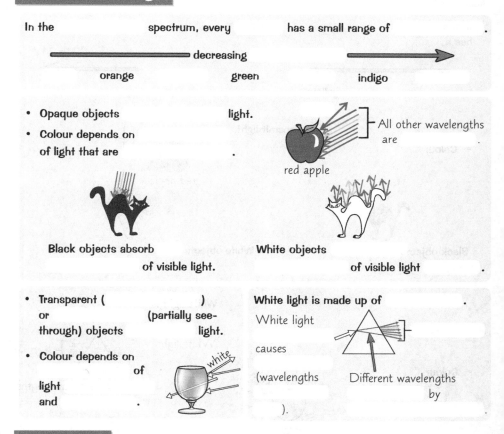

- Opaque objects   light.
- Colour depends on   of light that are   .

All other wavelengths are

red apple

Black objects absorb   of visible light.

White objects   of visible light   .

- Transparent (   ) or   (partially see-through) objects   light.
- Colour depends on   of   light and   .

White light is made up of   .

White light   causes   (wavelengths   ).

Different wavelengths   by   .

Colour Filters

Colour filters   (wavelengths) and   the rest.

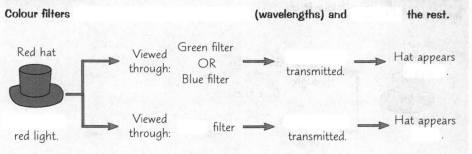

Red hat   Viewed through: Green filter OR Blue filter   →   transmitted.   →   Hat appears   .

red light.   Viewed through: filter →   transmitted.   →   Hat appears   .

     Section 2 — Waves and the Electromagnetic Spectrum

Colour

Colour and Wavelength

In the _____, every _____
has a _____.

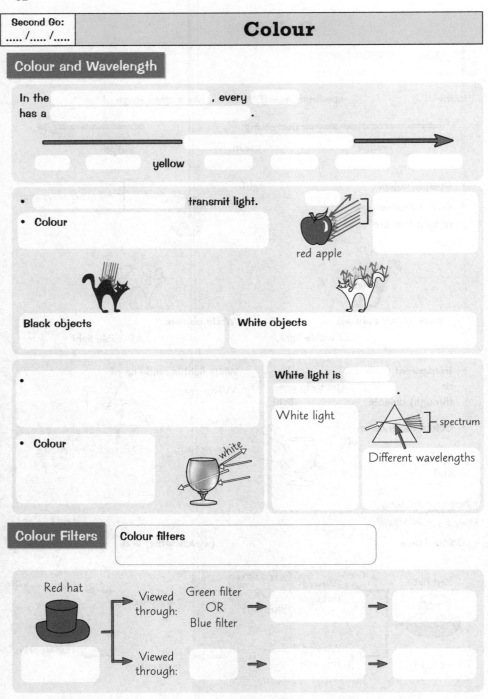

yellow

- _____ transmit light.
- Colour

red apple

Black objects

White objects

-

White light is _____

White light

spectrum

- Colour

white

Different wavelengths

Colour Filters

Colour filters

Red hat

Viewed through: Green filter OR Blue filter →

Viewed through: →

Section 2 — Waves and the Electromagnetic Spectrum

Lenses and Ray Diagrams

Images

REAL IMAGE	Image formed when light rays from a point on an object .
IMAGE	Image formed when light rays , but have actually come from another.

.... form images by ....

Converging Lenses

Converging lenses can produce   or   .

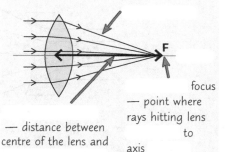

F

focus
— point where rays hitting lens   to   axis

— distance between centre of the lens and   axis

Diverging Lenses

Diverging lenses   produce   .

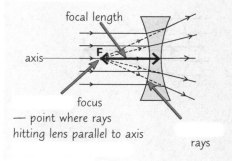

focal length

axis —— **F**

focus
— point where rays hitting lens parallel to axis

                rays

Lens Power

More   **the lens:**
- **More**   it converges/ diverges rays of light
- •   **the focal length**

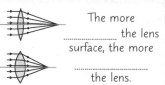

The more   the lens surface, the more .... the lens.

Converging lens = ...
Diverging lens = ...

Ray Diagram for Diverging Lenses

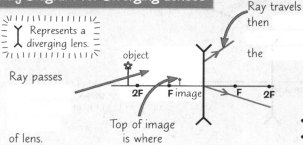

Y Represents a
Λ diverging lens.

Ray passes   of lens.

object

2F   F image   F   2F

Top of image is where

Ray travels   then   the   so it appears to have   on   side of the lens as the object.

Dotted line shows .... ray.

•   **image**
•
•   **than object**

Lenses and Ray Diagrams

Images

		....
REAL IMAGE		....
VIRTUAL IMAGE		....

by refracting

Converging Lenses

Converging lenses can

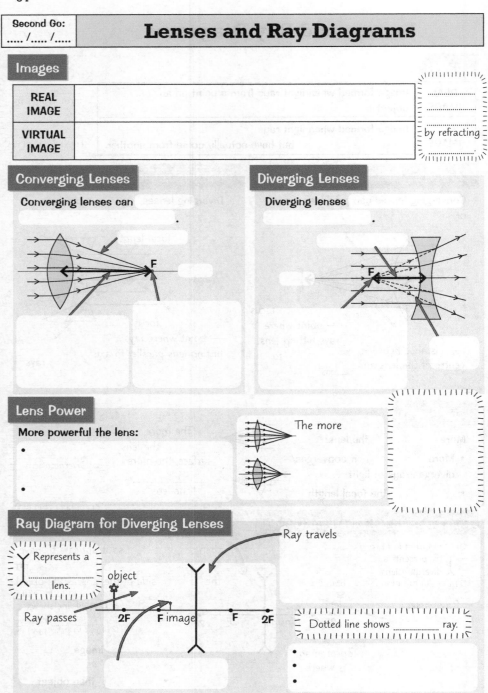

F

Diverging Lenses

Diverging lenses

F

Lens Power

More powerful the lens:

•

•

The more

Ray Diagram for Diverging Lenses

Represents a
.... lens.

object

Ray passes

2F   F image   F   2F

Ray travels

Dotted line shows .... ray.

•
•
•

Mixed Practice Quizzes

Bring your physics knowledge to light with some quiz questions on p.51-54.

Quiz 1
Date: ...... / ...... / ......

1) What colour filter would a red object need to be viewed through to appear red?
2) What symbol represents a diverging lens on a ray diagram?
3) Give the colours of the visible light spectrum in order of decreasing wavelength.
4) If an opaque object is yellow, is it reflecting or absorbing yellow light?
5) True or false? White objects absorb all wavelengths of visible light.
6) What is meant by a 'real image'?
7) Which type of lens brings together light rays that travel parallel to its axis?
8) Which can transmit light — opaque objects or translucent objects?
9) True or false? The more powerful a lens, the shorter its focal length.
10) True or false? The distance between the centre of a lens and the image it forms is the focal length.

Total:

Quiz 2
Date: ...... / ...... / ......

1) What is meant by the 'principal focus' of a converging lens?
2) True or false? Opaque objects transmit light.
3) Is the image formed by a diverging lens real or virtual?
4) Describe how the power of a lens is related to the curvature of its surface.
5) What happens to any wavelengths of light that are incident on an opaque white object?
6) True or false? Lenses form objects by refracting light.
7) What is meant by a 'virtual image'?
8) If an opaque object appears red, does it reflect or absorb blue wavelengths of light?
9) What do dotted lines on ray diagrams represent?
10) Is the power of a diverging lens positive or negative?

Total:

Section 2 — Waves and the Electromagnetic Spectrum

Mixed Practice Quizzes

Quiz 3   Date: ...... / ...... / ......

1) What does the colour of an opaque object depend on?

2) What is meant by the 'focal length' of a lens?

3) True or false? In the visible light spectrum,
each colour has a range of wavelengths.

4) True or false? The more powerful a lens,
the more strongly it converges (or diverges) rays of light.

5) Which type of lens will cause a ray travelling parallel to the axis
to refract away from the axis as it passes through the lens?

6) In terms of the reflection and absorption of visible light,
describe the difference between black objects and white objects.

7) Describe how the power of a lens is related to its focal length.

8) What do transparent and translucent objects both have in common?

9) Is red light, green light or no light transmitted when
a red object is viewed through a green filter?

10) Describe what happens when white light refracts.

Total:

Quiz 4   Date: ...... / ...... / ......

1) If a lens has a positive power, is it a converging or diverging lens?

2) If a red object is viewed through a blue filter, what colour will it appear?

3) True or false? Converging lenses always produce virtual images.

4) True or false? White objects reflect all wavelengths of visible light equally.

5) What do colour filters do?

6) Do lenses form images by reflecting or refracting light?

7) The distance between a lens' centre and its principal focus is called what?

8) What does the colour of a translucent object depend on?

9) True or false? Black objects don't absorb any wavelengths of visible light.

10) What does the ray diagram look like for
an object viewed through a diverging lens?

Total:

Section 2 — Waves and the Electromagnetic Spectrum

Ray Diagrams & EM Waves

Four Ray Diagrams for Converging Lenses

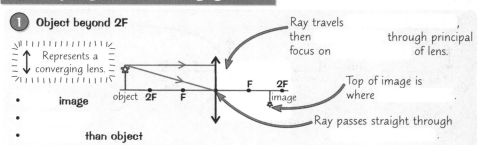

1 Object beyond 2F

Represents a converging lens.

Ray travels then _____ focus on _____ through principal _____ of lens.

Top of image is where _____

Ray passes straight through _____

• _____ image
• _____
• _____ than object

2 At 2F

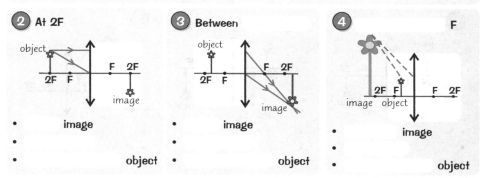

• _____ image
• _____
• _____ object

3 Between _____

• _____ image
• _____
• _____ object

4 _____ F

• _____
• _____
• _____ image _____ object

The Electromagnetic (EM) Spectrum

The EM spectrum is _____.

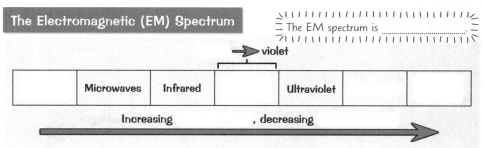

→ violet

	Microwaves	Infrared		Ultraviolet		

Increasing _____ , decreasing _____

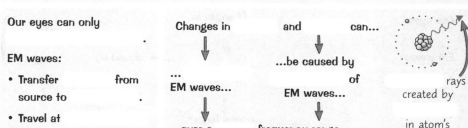

Our eyes can only _____ .

EM waves:
• Transfer _____ from source to _____ .
• Travel at _____ in a _____ .

Changes in _____ and _____ can...

...EM waves...

...over a _____

...be caused by _____ of EM waves...

...frequency range.

_____ rays created by _____ in atom's _____

Ray Diagrams & EM Waves

Four Ray Diagrams for Converging Lenses

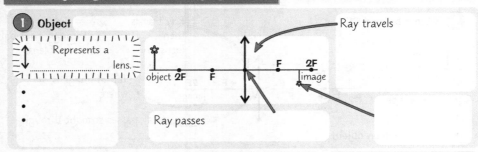

1 Object

Represents a .... lens.

-
-
-

Ray travels

object 2F F F 2F image

Ray passes

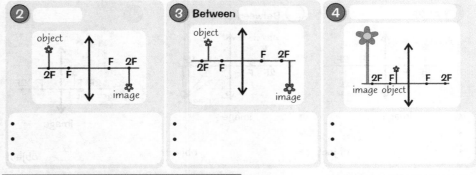

2

object
F 2F
2F F
image

-
-
-

3 Between

object
F 2F
2F F
image

-
-
-

4

2F F F 2F
image object

-
-
-

The Electromagnetic (EM) Spectrum

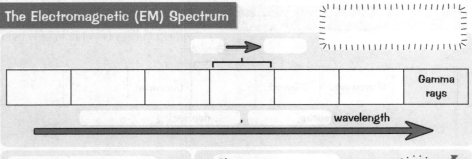

					Gamma rays

wavelength

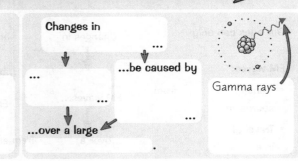

Our eyes

EM waves:
-
-

Changes in
...

...
...be caused by

...

...
...over a large

Gamma rays

Emitting and Absorbing EM Radiation

Temperature and Radiation

All objects _____ emit
and _____ EM radiation over
a _____ .

The _____ and _____
of wavelengths
depends on _____ .

~~~~~~~~~~~~~~~~~~~~~~~~~~~~~~
Intensity is .... per unit ....
~~~~~~~~~~~~~~~~~~~~~~~~~~~~~~

As object's _____ increases...
• Peak wavelength _____
• _____ of every emitted
wavelength increases.

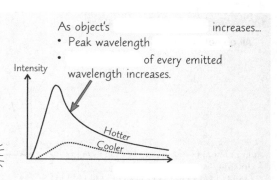

Intensity

Hotter
Cooler

Body at Constant Temperature

EM radiation   EM radiation

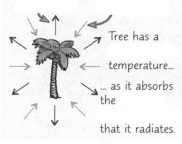

Tree has a _____

_____ temperature...

... as it absorbs the _____

that it radiates.

Body that is Changing Temperature

Ice cream's temperature ...

... as the average power it
absorbs is _____
the average power _____

~~~~~~~~~~~~~~~~~~~~~~~~~~~~~~
If _____ is
less than _____
body's temperature decreases.
~~~~~~~~~~~~~~~~~~~~~~~~~~~~~~

Radiation and Earth's Temperature

Daytime: Earth absorbs _____
_____ than it _____ .

⬇

Local temperature _____ .

Nighttime: Earth _____
more radiation than it _____ .

⬇

Local temperature _____ .

~~~~~~~~~~~~~~~~~~~~~~~~~~~~~~
Overall, temperature of Earth
....
~~~~~~~~~~~~~~~~~~~~~~~~~~~~~~

Radiation emitted by _____ ,
_____ and Earth's surface.

Some radiation _____

Atmosphere

Earth's surface

Some radiation from _____
by atmosphere, clouds and _____

Second Go:
..... / ..... / .....

Emitting and Absorbing EM Radiation

Temperature and Radiation

All objects continually

As object's

•

•

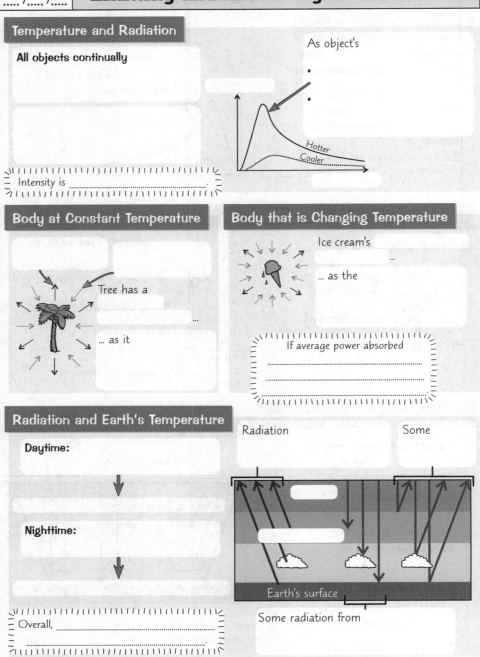

Hotter
Cooler

Intensity is ....

Body at Constant Temperature

Tree has a

...

... as it

Body that is Changing Temperature

Ice cream's ...

... as the

If average power absorbed
....
....
....

Radiation and Earth's Temperature

Daytime:

Nighttime:

Radiation   Some

Earth's surface

Overall, ...
....

Some radiation from

Uses and Dangers of EM Waves

Producing Radio Waves

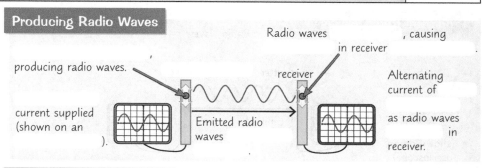

Radio waves   , causing
                                            in receiver

producing radio waves.   ,

                                                    receiver

current supplied
(shown on an   )   Emitted radio
                                          waves

Alternating
current of

as radio waves
                    in
receiver.

Some Uses of EM Waves

Radio waves   light
•   •
• Communications   • _____ ovens   • Illumination
•   transmissions   •   •
                                               •   transmissions

Infrared radiation   UV waves
• Electric   •   systems   •   lamps
• Cooking   • TV   • Security
•   imaging •   •   forged bank notes
• Optical   communications   •   water

X-rays   _____ rays
•   X-rays   • Detecting and
• Airport   •   food and   equipment
• Looking   objects

Dangers of EM Waves

Types of _____ radiation.	Danger of excessive exposure	
	Microwaves	
		causes skin _____
	Ultraviolet	• causes _____ on surface of skin, which can lead to _____ • damages _____ , possibly causing _____ conditions or _____
		causes _____ damage or _____ , which can lead to _____
	_____ rays	

possible _____
increases,
_____ increases

     Section 2 — Waves and the Electromagnetic Spectrum

62

Uses and Dangers of EM Waves

Producing Radio Waves

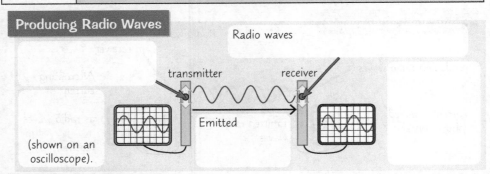

Radio waves

transmitter   receiver

Emitted

(shown on an oscilloscope).

Some Uses of EM Waves

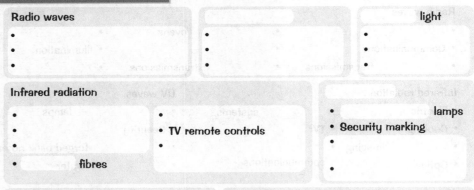

Radio waves
-
-
-

light
-
-
-

Infrared radiation
-
-
-
-          fibres

- TV remote controls
-

- lamps
- Security marking
-
-

X-rays
-
-
-          objects

rays
-
- Sterilising

Dangers of EM Waves

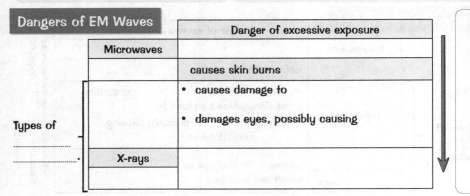

		Danger of excessive exposure
	Microwaves	
		causes skin burns
Types of		• causes damage to • damages eyes, possibly causing
	X-rays	

Section 2 — Waves and the Electromagnetic Spectrum

Mixed Practice Quizzes

Wave goodbye to Section 2 with these quiz questions, which cover p.57-62.

Quiz 1   Date: ...... / ...... / ......

1) Give one use of: a) x-rays, b) gamma rays.
2) Explain why the Earth's local temperature increases during the day.
3) True or false? The EM spectrum is continuous.
4) Name a type of EM wave that can be used for broadcasting.
5) What does the distribution and intensity of the EM wavelengths emitted by an object depend on?
6) True or false? An alternating current can be used to generate radio waves.
7) Give two dangers of excessive exposure to ultraviolet radiation.
8) What type of EM wave has the lowest frequency?
9) True or false? An object at a constant temperature absorbs the same average power as it radiates.
10) A converging lens produces a virtual image when an object is placed where?

Total:

Quiz 2   Date: ...... / ...... / ......

1) Describe what happens to the intensity of the wavelengths of EM radiation an object emits as the temperature of that object increases.
2) What symbol represents a converging lens on a ray diagram?
3) True or false? Gamma rays can be made by changes in an atom's nucleus.
4) Which two types of EM wave can be used for satellite transmissions?
5) Describe how the amount of radiation the Earth absorbs and emits affects its local temperature.
6) Why are gamma rays potentially the most dangerous type of EM wave?
7) True or false? EM waves transfer energy from absorber to source.
8) If an object's temperature is rising, will the average power it radiates be more or less than the average power it absorbs?
9) Give two uses of visible light.
10) What type of EM wave lies between radio waves and infrared on the EM spectrum?

Total:

Mixed Practice Quizzes

Quiz 3   Date: ...... / ...... / ......

1) Describe one danger of excessive exposure to X-rays.

2) Give the EM spectrum in order of increasing frequency.

3) Explain why the Earth's local temperature decreases at nighttime.

4) True or false? If the average power an object absorbs
   is less than it radiates, its temperature will be constant.

5) What does the ray diagram look like for an object viewed through
   a converging lens when the object is further than 2F from the lens?

6) How are radio waves produced?

7) Describe the difference in intensity between the EM wavelengths
   emitted from a hot object compared to a cooler object.

8) True or false? Changes in atoms and nuclei can generate
   EM waves over a large frequency range.

9) Give three uses of UV waves.

10) Describe the image produced by a converging lens for an object placed at 2F.

Total:

Quiz 4   Date: ...... / ...... / ......

1) Name a type of EM wave that can cause skin burns.

2) State two ways that clouds prevent radiation reaching the Earth's surface.

3) Give five uses of infrared radiation.

4) True or false? All objects continually emit and absorb EM radiation.

5) Describe the image formed when an object placed somewhere between
   F and 2F away from a converging lens is viewed through the lens.

6) True or false? Higher frequency EM waves travel faster in a vacuum.

7) Between radio waves and gamma rays, which has:
   a) the shortest frequency? b) the shortest wavelength?

8) Will the peak wavelength of the EM waves emitted by a hot object be
   higher or lower than the peak wavelength emitted by a cooler object?

9) Which two types of EM wave can be used for cooking food?

10) What is the only type of EM wave that our eyes can detect?

Total:

Section 2 — Waves and the Electromagnetic Spectrum

The Model of the Atom

The History of the Atom

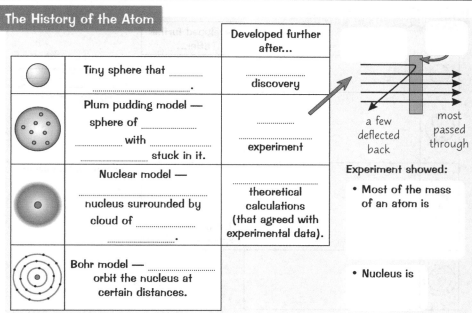

		Developed further after...
	Tiny sphere that	.... discovery
	Plum pudding model — sphere of .... with .... stuck in it.	.... experiment
	Nuclear model — .... nucleus surrounded by cloud of	.... theoretical calculations (that agreed with experimental data).
	Bohr model — .... orbit the nucleus at certain distances.	

a few deflected back

most passed through

Experiment showed:

• Most of the mass of an atom is

• Nucleus is

The Current Model of the Atom

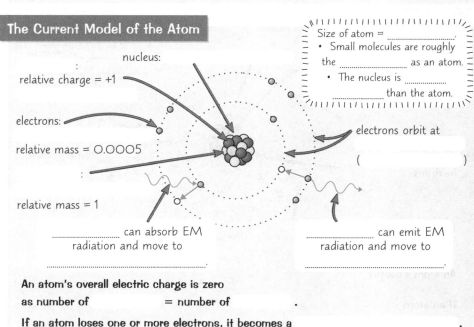

nucleus:

relative charge = +1

electrons:

relative mass = 0.0005

:

relative mass = 1

.... can absorb EM radiation and move to

....

Size of atom ≈ ....
• Small molecules are roughly the .... as an atom.
• The nucleus is .... than the atom.

electrons orbit at

( )

.... can emit EM radiation and move to

....

An atom's overall electric charge is zero as number of .... = number of ....

If an atom loses one or more electrons, it becomes a ....

The Model of the Atom

The History of the Atom

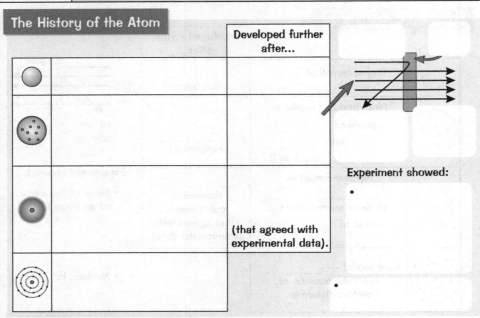

		Developed further after...
		(that agreed with experimental data).

Experiment showed:

-

-

The Current Model of the Atom

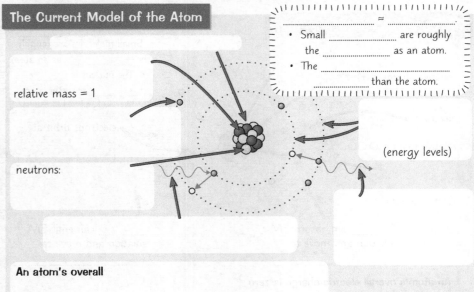

.... ≈ ....
- Small .... are roughly the .... as an atom.
- The ....
.... than the atom.

relative mass = 1

(energy levels)

neutrons:

An atom's overall

If an atom

Isotopes and Radioactive Decay

Mass Number and Atomic Number

ISOTOPES of an element — atoms with the same number of .... but different numbers of .... (and so different ....).

All atoms of each element have a set number of ....

$$^{16}_{8}\text{O}$$

total number of .... and .... in an atom.

number of .... (equal to .... in an atom of nucleus).

Radioactive Decay

RADIOACTIVE DECAY — when the nucleus of an .... decays, giving out .... to become more stable.

IONISING RADIATION (α, β^-, β^+ and γ) — radiation that knocks .... off atoms, creating ....

Unstable nuclei can also release .... when they decay.

	alpha (α)	beta minus (β^-)	gamma (γ)
Consists of...	2 .... and 2 .... (..................... nucleus)	fast-moving .... from nucleus	.... from nucleus
Absorbed by...	Sheet of	Sheet of	Thick sheets ....
Range in air	Few	Few	
Ionising power	....	Moderate	....

A positron (β^+) has same mass as an .... , but a relative charge of .... It is ejected from the nucleus in ....

Nuclear Equations

.... and .... on each side of a nuclear equation must balance.

α-decay
• mass number decreases by 4
• atomic number ....

$$^{238}_{92}\text{U} \longrightarrow \text{Th} + {}^{4}_{2}\alpha$$

neutron emission
• mass no. ....
• atomic no. stays the same

γ-decay
• mass no. and atomic no. ....

When particles in nucleus rearrange due to decay, ...

β^--decay
• mass no. ....
• atomic no. increases by 1 — ....

$$^{14}_{6}\text{C} \longrightarrow \text{N} + {}^{0}_{-1}\beta$$

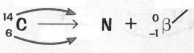

β^+-decay
• mass no. ....
• atomic no. decreases by 1 — ....

$$^{18}_{9}\text{F} \longrightarrow \text{O} + {}^{0}_{1}\beta$$

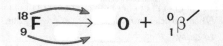

Section 3 — Radioactivity and Astronomy

Isotopes and Radioactive Decay

Mass Number and Atomic Number

ISOTOPES of an element — ....
....
....

All atoms of each element have ....
....

$$^{16}_{8}O$$

Radioactive Decay

RADIOACTIVE DECAY — ....
....

IONISING RADIATION (α, β^-, β^+ and γ) — ....
....

	(α)	(β^-)	(γ)
Consists of...			
Absorbed by...			
Range in air			
Ionising power			

A ....
(β^+) has ....
....
as an electron,
but a
....
....
of +1.
It is ....
.... in
β^+ decay.

Nuclear Equations

.... of ....
a nuclear equation ....

α-decay
- ....
- atomic number ....

$$^{238}_{92}U \longrightarrow \quad Th + \quad /$$

neutron   • mass no. ....
emission   • .... stays the same

γ-decay
• ....

When particles in nucleus .... due
to decay, ...

β^--decay
• mass no. ....
• ....

$$^{14}_{6}C \longrightarrow \quad N + \quad /$$

β^+-decay
• mass no. ....
• ....

$$^{18}_{9}F \longrightarrow \quad O + \quad /$$

Radioactivity

Activity

Radioactive decay is
Can't say if or when a

ACTIVITY — the   at which a source
decays,

Radioactive decays can be detected
by ....

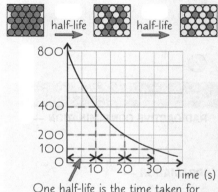

A Geiger-
Muller tube
and counter
measures

Background Radiation

BACKGROUND RADIATION —
that's
              .

Two types of sources:

1. From Earth —   , food,   ,
          , nuclear
   waste, fallout from nuclear explosions.

2. From space —   .

Contamination and Irradiation

RADIOACTIVE CONTAMINATION —
getting unwanted radioactive atoms
                    .

IRRADIATION — the
              to ionising radiation
(doesn't make the object   ).

Half-life

HALF-LIFE — time taken for

              to halve.

half-life   half-life

800
400
200
100
0   10   20   30
                    Time (s)
One half-life is the time taken for
              of a sample to halve.

Risk of Radiation

radiation
can enter a
living cell,   cell can be

              can multiply and
              become

cell can be

Inside body:
-          is most dangerous
-          is least dangerous

Outside body:
-          is most dangerous
-          is least dangerous

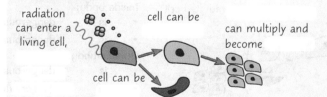

Three precautions to
reduce exposure:

1. Keep sources in
                    .

2.   barriers 3.
   or be in a   and use tongs
   to the source.   to   .

People exposed to radiation (e.g. ....
.........................) should have their exposure ....

Second Go: ...../...../.....

Radioactivity

Radioactive decays can be ....

Activity

Can't say

ACTIVITY —

A

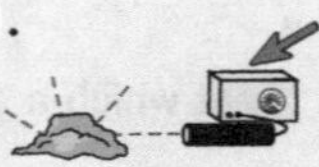

A .... measures ....

Background Radiation

BACKGROUND RADIATION —

Two types of sources:

1

2

Half-life

HALF-LIFE —

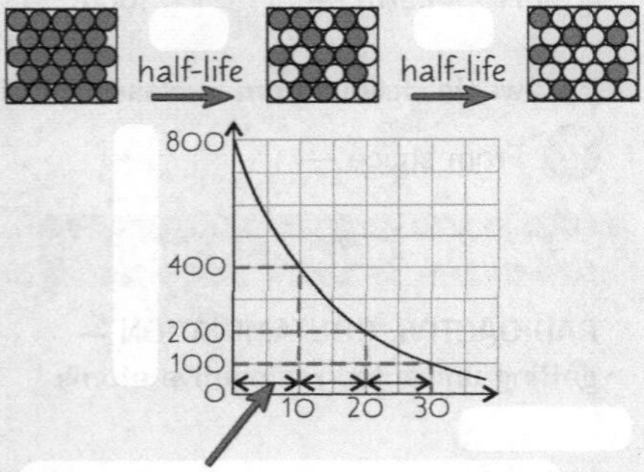

half-life
half-life
800
400
200
100
0
10
20
30

Contamination and Irradiation

RADIOACTIVE CONTAMINATION —

IRRADIATION —

Risk of Radiation

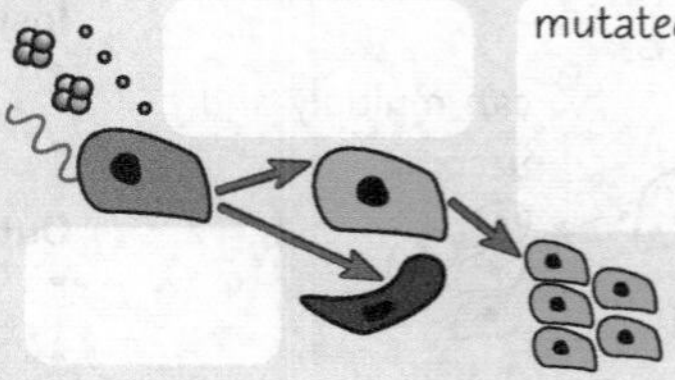

mutated cell

Inside body:

- is dangerous
- is dangerous

Outside body:

- is dangerous
- is dangerous

Three precautions to reduce :

1

2

3

Uses of Radiation

Half-life and Hazards

half-life $\rightarrow$ activity falls $\rightarrow$ emits high amounts of radiation in $\rightarrow$ becomes safe

half-life $\rightarrow$ activity falls $\rightarrow$ emits small amounts of radiation over $\rightarrow$ hazardous for a

Thickness Gauging

β^- by
thin materials (e.g. paper).

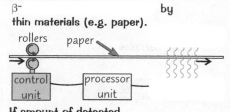

rollers   paper

control unit   processor unit

If amount of detected
radiation changes,
has changed, so rollers   .

Two Ways to Treat Cancer

1. Externally —
   from outside body directed
   at cancer cells.
2. Internally —
                put inside body
   next to cancer cells.
   Treatments cause damage to both
   ....

Medical Tracers

Medical tracer (radioactive source)
                          to
explore internal organs.

 outside the body.

                    used so that
radiation passes out of body

Fire Alarms

                        in fire alarm
causes ionisation and current.
Smoke particles
                , and cause alarm to sound.

Sterilisation

High doses of   kills microbes.
So   used to
                food and medical equipment.

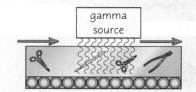

gamma source

PET Scans

PET scans use
                as tracer.

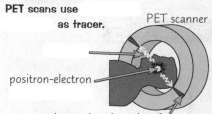

PET scanner

positron-electron

γ-rays detected and used to form

                sources have very
half-lives, so must be produced nearby.

Both of these can be used to ...., e.g. cancer.

72

Uses of Radiation

Half-life and Hazards

→   →   →   in short time   →

→   →   over long time   →

Thickness Gauging

control unit — processor unit — detector

If amount of detected _____, has changed, so rollers adjusted.

Two Ways to Treat Cancer

1

2

Treatments cause _____ .

Medical Tracers

Gamma sources

Fire Alarms

Smoke particles

Sterilisation

So gamma radiation used

gamma source

PET Scans

and used to

form _____

sources have _____ half-lives, so must be produced _____ .

Both of these can be used to _____

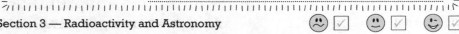

Nuclear Fission and Fusion

Nuclear Fission

NUCLEAR FISSION — splitting a

into   of approximately equal size.

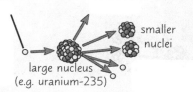

smaller
nuclei

large nucleus
(e.g. uranium-235)

Released   can
be absorbed by another
nucleus, starting a

...

... controlled in   .

Nuclear Reactors

Boron control rod — absorbs
                          to
control chain reaction.
Prevents runaway reaction that
could cause an   .

Boiler —

to steam. Steam drives
turbine and generator to
make   .

— slows down
neutrons so they
can be

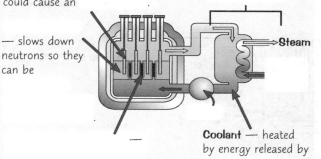

→ Steam

Coolant — heated
by energy released by

Pros & Cons of Nuclear Power

➕ **No**   emissions

➕ **A lot of energy from**

        of fuel

➕

➖ **Has a**
        public perception

➖ **Waste is**
        and hard to safely
        dispose of

➖

Nuclear Fusion

NUCLEAR FUSION — ....
.... collide at high
speed and join to create a
....

Energy — some of the
        of the   is
converted into energy
        and released.
heavier nucleus

Fusion only happens at   , as
nuclei have to overcome   to get close enough to fuse.
Making these conditions on Earth needs a lot of energy and is   ...
... so not yet built an efficient   .

Nuclear Fission and Fusion

Nuclear Fission

NUCLEAR FISSION — ....
....
....

Fission usually occurs after

...

...

Nuclear Reactors

control rod — absorbs
.... to
control ....
Prevents ....
that could cause an ....

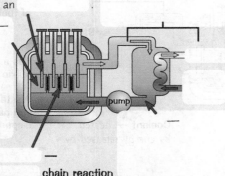

Boiler — coolant heats

chain reaction

Pros & Cons of Nuclear Power

✚ ....

✚ **A** ....
from small amount

✚ ....

– **Has a** ....

– ....

– ....

Nuclear Fusion

NUCLEAR FUSION — ....
....
....
....

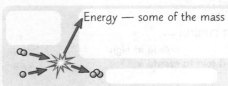

Energy — some of the mass

Fusion only happens at

Making these conditions

Mixed Practice Quizzes

Before all that revision from p.65-74 decays out of your brain, have a go at these quizzes. When you finish each quiz, work out your total score.

Quiz 1

Date: ...... / ...... / ......

1) Give one disadvantage of using nuclear power to generate electricity.

2) True or false? The mass number of a nucleus decreases by 4 when it emits an alpha particle.

3) Explain why gamma sources are used in medical tracers.

4) True or false? The nucleus of an atom is negatively charged.

5) Which has the longest range in air — alpha, beta minus or gamma radiation?

6) What is the approximate size of an atom?

7) What type of ionising radiation is used to sterilise medical equipment?

8) What name is given to the number of protons in an atom?

9) Which type of ionising radiation is most dangerous inside the body?

10) What is the role of the moderator in a nuclear reactor?

Total:

Quiz 2

Date: ...... / ...... / ......

1) What does an electron need to absorb to move to a higher energy level in an atom?

2) What are isotopes of an element?

3) True or false? Mass may be converted into energy during nuclear fusion.

4) Why do the positron sources used in PET scans need to be made near where they are used?

5) Which type of ionising radiation is equivalent to a helium nucleus?

6) What is meant by irradiation?

7) True or false? One half-life is the time taken for the activity of a sample to fall to half of its initial level.

8) Give one advantage of using nuclear power to generate electricity.

9) What happens to the atomic number of a nucleus when it emits a positron?

10) Give two examples of sources of background radiation from Earth.

Total:

Section 3 — Radioactivity and Astronomy

Mixed Practice Quizzes

Quiz 3   Date: ...... / ...... / ......

1) True or false? When a nucleus emits gamma radiation, its atomic number decreases.

2) Name a device that can be used to detect radioactive decay.

3) What is the relative charge of an electron?

4) What did the alpha particle scattering experiment prove about the atom?

5) What types of radioactive sources can be used to treat cancer internally?

6) True or false? If an atom loses an electron it becomes a negatively charged ion.

7) What does the mass number of an atom tell you?

8) Give one precaution you could take to reduce your exposure to radiation when using radioactive sources.

9) What particle can trigger nuclear fission when it is absorbed by a large nucleus?

10) Which type of ionising radiation has the strongest ionising power?

Total:

Quiz 4   Date: ...... / ...... / ......

1) True or false? All atoms of the same element have the same number of neutrons.

2) True or false? An isotope with a long half-life will quickly become safe.

3) Give one use of alpha radiation.

4) What is meant by the activity of a radioactive source?

5) Describe how beta minus sources are used in thickness gauging.

6) What is used to control the chain reaction in a nuclear reactor?

7) During which type of radioactive decay does a neutron in the nucleus turn into a proton?

8) Why haven't efficient nuclear fusion power stations been built on Earth yet?

9) What is meant by radioactive contamination?

10) Describe the plum pudding model of the atom.

Total:

The Solar System and Gravity

Our Solar System

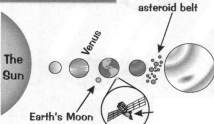

asteroid belt

DISTANCE FROM SUN →

Venus · Saturn · Uranus

The Sun

Earth's Moon

Plus many more ...., dwarf planets, ... and ....

- The .... planets orbit the .... (our star) in ....
- Moons are .... that orbit ....
  Our moon .... in ....
- Artificial satellites usually .... in ....
- Comets orbit the .... in ....
  They travel faster .... to the Sun.

Changing Ideas of the Solar System

1000s of years ago	.... model	Everything orbits around ....
....	.... model	Planets ....

Circular Orbits

.... keeps planets and satellites in circular orbits.

It causes the object's .... to constantly ....

This means the object's .... constantly ....

The object's .... remains ....

Gravitational Field Strength

Gravitational field strength, g, of a body (e.g. a planet) depends on two things:

1 .... of the body.
.... = bigger g.

2 .... from it.
.... = smaller g.

Weight is .... to g.
A mass has .... on different bodies.

Stable Orbits

If the .... of an object in a stable orbit changes, the .... of the orbit changes.

The smaller the orbit .... , the .... the object must travel.

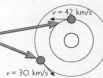

$v = 42$ km/s

$v = 30$ km/s

The Solar System and Gravity

Our Solar System

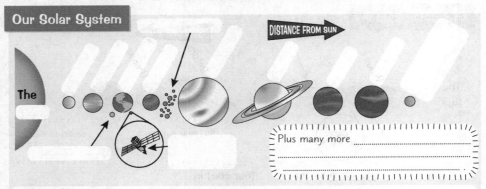

DISTANCE FROM SUN

The

Plus many more ....
....

- The eight
- Moons are

- Artificial
- Comets

Changing Ideas of the Solar System

.... ago	.... model	orbits around ....
.... model	orbit	

Gravitational Field Strength

Gravitational field strength, g, of a body (e.g. a planet) depends on two things:

1

2

Weight is

Circular Orbits

Gravitational force

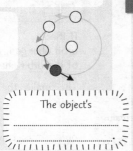

The object's
....
....

Stable Orbits

The smaller

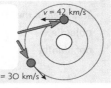

$v = 42$ km/s

$v = 30$ km/s

The Universe: Theories & Evidence

Doppler Effect

When a wave source is _____, there is a change in the _____.

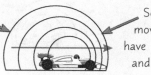

Sound waves from source moving _____ from observer have _____ and _____.

Sound waves from source moving _____ observer have _____ and _____.

Red-Shift

RED-SHIFT — an observed _____ in the _____ of light (light is shifted towards the _____ end of the _____).
Observed when a galaxy moves _____.

The more _____ the galaxy:
- the _____ it moves away from us
- the _____ its red-shift

The light observed from most galaxies is _____, so most galaxies are _____ _____ from us.

CMB Radiation

COSMIC _____

(CMB) RADIATION — _____ frequency _____ radiation coming from _____ parts of the _____.

Two Theories for the Creation of the Universe

Theory	Three things the theory says about the Universe	Red-shift	CMB radiation
.... theory	1 Universe has _____ age. 2 All matter started in a _____ and _____ tiny space and _____. 3 Space started _____ and _____.	Evidence that the Universe is _____.	Evidence the Universe had a _____. Supports _____.
Steady State theory	1 Universe _____ and _____ — no _____ or _____. 2 Universe is _____. 3 More matter _____ — density _____.	Supports _____.	Can't be _____. Doesn't _____ theory.

Big Bang theory is _____ for how the Universe began as both _____ and _____ support it.

Section 3 — Radioactivity and Astronomy

Second Go:
...../...../.....

The Universe: Theories & Evidence

Doppler Effect

When a wave source is

Red-Shift

RED-SHIFT —

The more _____ the galaxy:

•

•

The light observed _____

CMB Radiation

Two Theories for the Creation of the Universe

Theory	Three things the theory says about the Universe	Red-shift	CMB radiation
1 2 3		Evidence that	Evidence
1 2 3			

Big Bang theory is

Stars and Looking into Space

The Life Cycle of a Star

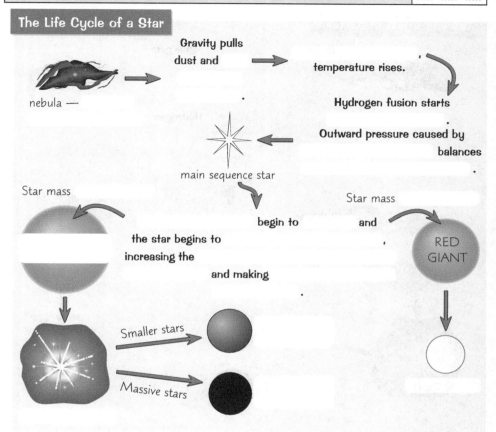

nebula —

Gravity pulls dust and

temperature rises.

Hydrogen fusion starts

Outward pressure caused by balances

main sequence star

Star mass

begin to

Star mass

and

RED GIANT

the star begins to increasing the and making

Smaller stars

Massive stars

Observing the Universe

From 1600s → **From 1930s** → **From 1960s**

telescopes:

- telescopes
- Only detect

Telescopes for other

(e.g.

).

Telescopes put

Two reasons to put telescopes   :

1 To avoid

2 To detect   that would be

Telescopes and .... improved over time to give .... / .... and ....

Section 3 — Radioactivity and Astronomy

| Second Go:
...... /...... /...... | **Stars and Looking into Space** |

The Life Cycle of a Star

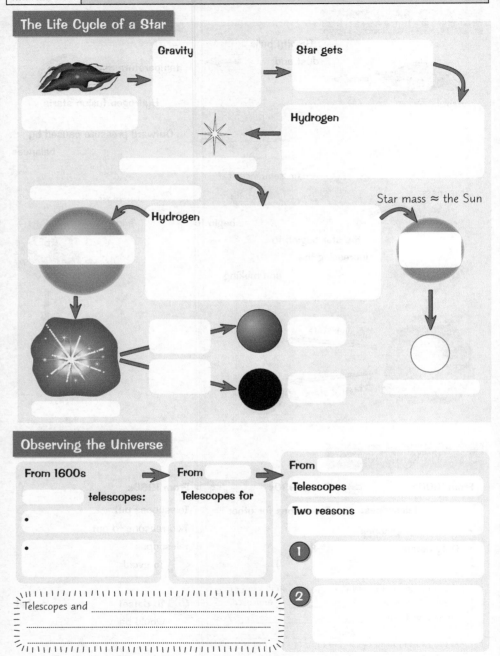

Gravity → Star gets

Hydrogen

Hydrogen

Star mass ≈ the Sun

Observing the Universe

From 1600s → From → From

telescopes:

Telescopes for

Telescopes

Two reasons

•

•

1

2

Telescopes and ....
....
....

Section 3 — Radioactivity and Astronomy

Mixed Practice Quizzes

Reinforce your universal knowledge by answering questions on p.77-82 below.

Quiz 1   Date: ...... / ...... / ......

1) True or false? Faster planets in stable orbits have larger orbital radii than slower planets in stable orbits.
2) What is red-shift?
3) How is a galaxy's distance related to the amount its light is red-shifted?
4) What is cosmic microwave background (CMB) radiation?
5) True or false? A planet's gravitational field strength depends only on how far away you are from the planet.
6) Describe the life cycle of a star that has the same mass as the Sun.
7) True or false? Moons orbit planets.
8) Explain how red-shift measurements support the Big Bang theory.
9) Name the planets of the solar system, in order of increasing distance from the Sun.
10) What causes the main sequence stage of a star's life cycle to end?

Total:

Quiz 2   Date: ...... / ...... / ......

1) True or false? The Sun will become a neutron star in the future.
2) How have methods of observing objects in space changed over time?
3) True or false? The further away a galaxy, the faster it moves away from us.
4) How does the observed wavelength compare to the source wavelength for a wave source moving away from an observer?
5) What determines whether a star becomes a red giant or a red supergiant?
6) What force keeps planets and satellites in their orbits?
7) What is a nebula?
8) Which property — direction, velocity or speed — remains constant for an object in a circular orbit?
9) True or false? A mass has the same weight everywhere in the Universe.
10) Describe the Steady State theory of the Universe.

Total:

Mixed Practice Quizzes

Quiz 3 Date: ...... / ...... / ......

1) How many planets orbit the Sun?

2) Name both possible stages of a star's life cycle after a supernova.

3) Briefly describe how our ideas about the orbits of planets have changed through time.

4) True or false? The Sun is a star in our solar system.

5) Why does cosmic microwave background radiation provide evidence for the Big Bang theory but not for the Steady State theory?

6) True or false? Artificial satellites usually orbit the Sun in elliptical orbits.

7) What balances the inward force of gravity in a main sequence star?

8) Explain why a mass would have different weights on different planets.

9) Describe how the Universe began, according to the Big Bang theory.

10) State two properties that constantly change for a satellite in a circular orbit.

Total:

Quiz 4 Date: ...... / ...... / ......

1) Does a galaxy have to be moving towards or away from the Earth for us to observe a red-shift from it?

2) What was the initial state of the Universe, according to the Big Bang theory?

3) Describe how the Sun was formed.

4) Describe the life cycle of a star that has a much larger mass than the Sun.

5) What happens to the radius of a planet's orbit if the speed of the planet decreases but the orbit remains stable?

6) Describe the orbits of comets in the solar system.

7) Give one advantage of using a telescope that is located in space, rather than on Earth, to observe objects in space.

8) True or false? It was once believed that the Sun orbited the Earth.

9) What is the currently accepted model for the origin of the Universe?

10) True or false? Electrostatic forces keep artificial satellites in circular orbits.

Total:

Work Done, Power and Forces

Work Done

Work done = _____

When a force moves an object from one point to another, work is done on the object and energy is _____ .

work done (J)
(1 joule = _____)

force (N)

$$E = \_\_\_ \; d$$

distance moved (m)

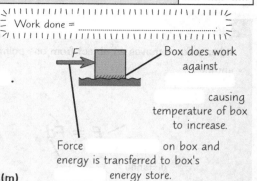

Box does work against _____

causing temperature of box to increase.

Force _____ on box and energy is transferred to box's energy store.

Power

POWER — _____
(or rate of doing work).

One watt (W) = one _____ of energy _____ .

2 W motor transfers _____ than 1 W motor, so lifts mass faster.

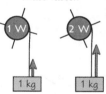

power
( )

(or _____) (J)

$$P = \frac{E}{t}$$

(s)

Force Basics

FORCE — a push or a pull on an object caused by it _____ .

When two objects interact, they exert an _____ on each other. This pair of forces is _____ .

Two types of forces:

1 _____ : objects have to be touching.
- friction
- _____
- normal contact force

2 _____ : objects don't need to be touching.
- gravitational force
- _____
- _____

Section 4 — Forces and Energy

| Second Go:
...... /...... /...... | **Work Done, Power and Forces** |

Work Done

Work done = ...

When a force moves an object from one point to another,

$$E = Fd$$

distance

(m)

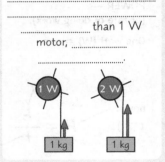

Box
against

causing

Force   on box and

to box's   energy store.

Power

POWER —

One watt (W) =

(or   ) ( )

$$P = \frac{\qquad}{time\ taken\ (s)}$$

....
....
.... than 1 W
motor, ...
....

1 W   2 W

1 kg   1 kg

Force Basics

FORCE —

When two objects interact,

Two types of forces:

1

-
- air resistance
-

2

-
-
- magnetic force

Section 4 — Forces and Energy

Forces

Vectors

.... , and other vectors, can
be represented visually as ....

Direction of arrow shows
....

Length of arrow shows ....

Free Body Force Diagrams

FREE BODY FORCE DIAGRAM — shows
all forces acting on an ....

drag

weight

Arrows show relative

.... and ....
of forces acting.

Resolving Forces

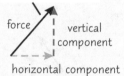

force

vertical
component

horizontal component

.... forces acting
together have ....
.... as the single
.... force.

Equilibrium

EQUILIBRIUM — when the forces
acting on an object are
.... and the resultant force
....

Object in ....

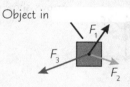

F_1

F_3

F_2

Drawing forces .... in
scale drawing creates
a ....

F_1

F_2

F_3

Two Ways to Calculate Resultant Force

RESULTANT (NET) FORCE — a .... **force**
that can ....
on an object to give the ....
as all the original forces acting together.

1 Add forces pointing in
.... Subtract forces pointing
in ....

F_1 F_2

.... = resultant force

2

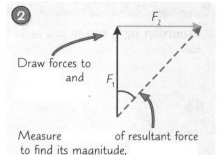

F_2

F_1

Draw forces to
.... and ....

Measure .... of resultant force
to find its magnitude,
.... to find its direction.

Forces

Vectors

_____ , and other vectors, can be _____ _____ .

Direction of arrow shows
....
....

Free Body Force Diagrams

FREE BODY FORCE DIAGRAM —

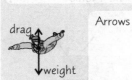

Arrows show relative

Equilibrium

EQUILIBRIUM —

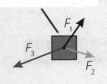

Drawing forces

Resolving Forces

Component forces

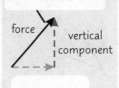

Two Ways to Calculate Resultant Force

RESULTANT (NET) FORCE — a single force that can

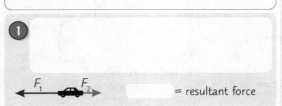

①

_____ = resultant force

②

Draw

Measure

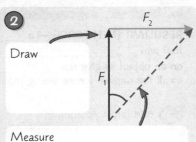

Moments

Calculating Moments

MOMENT —
of a force.

moment
of a force =   **(N)**   × normal to the
( )   direction of the
force ( )

Force applied at

( )

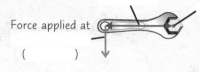

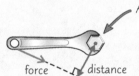

force --- distance

Applying same force at

means a smaller
normal distance so a
smaller .

Moments in Equilibrium

PRINCIPLE OF MOMENTS —
If object is in equilibrium,

=

about a pivot.

Smaller mass produces
...

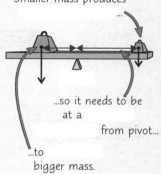

...so it needs to be
at a
from pivot...

...to
bigger mass.

Gears

GEARS — used to transmit
the
from one
place to another.

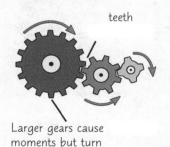

teeth

Larger gears cause
moments but turn
.

Levers

LEVERS — make it easier
.

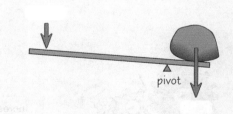

pivot

between pivot
and applied force.

Less
required to
get the same

Easier to

.

Moments

Calculating Moments

MOMENT —

$$\underset{\text{(Nm)}}{\boxed{}} = \frac{\text{force}}{(\ \ )} \times \boxed{}$$

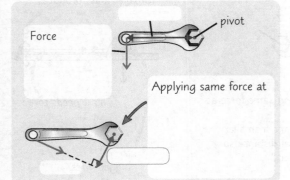

Force

pivot

Applying same force at

Moments in Equilibrium

PRINCIPLE OF MOMENTS —

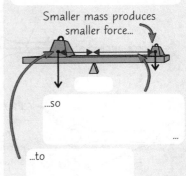

Smaller mass produces
smaller force...

...so

...

...to

Gears

GEARS —

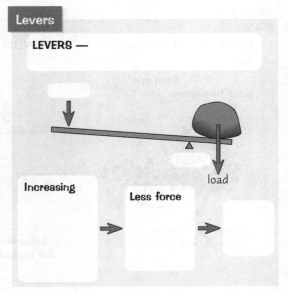

Levers

LEVERS —

Increasing

Less force

load

Mixed Practice Quizzes

You've really got some good work done over the last few pages. Time to put your knowledge to the test with some quiz questions covering p.85-90.

Quiz 1

Date: ...... / ...... / ......

1) Give the equation that links power, work done and time taken.
2) Describe how using a lever could make lifting a load easier.
3) True or false? Force is a vector quantity.
4) What is the equation for calculating the moment of a force?
5) Give two examples of contact forces.
6) What does *d* stand for in the formula for calculating work done?
7) What type of drawing can be used for resolving forces?
8) In terms of the forces acting on an object, what does it mean when an object is said to be in equilibrium?
9) 1 newton metre is equal to how many joules of work?
10) True or false? Larger gears cause smaller moments.

Total:

Quiz 2

Date: ...... / ...... / ......

1) What is a force?
2) Define the moment of a force.
3) Describe how to find the resultant force of two forces that don't act along the same line.
4) What type of diagram shows all the forces acting on an isolated body?
5) Give two examples of non-contact forces.
6) What is the resultant force acting on an object in equilibrium?
7) True or false? A 2 W motor would lift a 1 kg mass faster than a 1 W motor.
8) If an object is in equilibrium, what must be true about the moments acting on it?
9) True or false? Gears are used to transmit the rotational effect of a force from one place to another.
10) What are the units for work done?

Total:

Mixed Practice Quizzes

Quiz 3   Date: ...... / ...... / ......

1) True or false? When a force moves an object along a surface from one point to another, the object does work against frictional forces.

2) What is one joule of energy per second in watts?

3) Give the units for the moment of a force.

4) What is meant by a resultant force?

5) What does the length of a vector arrow tell you about the vector quantity?

6) Describe the difference between contact and non-contact forces.

7) How would you calculate the resultant force acting on an object if all the forces acting on it are on the same line?

8) How does a lever reduce the force required to get the same moment?

9) If all the forces acting on an object in equilibrium are drawn tip-to-tail in a scale drawing, will they create a closed loop or an open loop?

10) What is the equation for the work done when a force moves an object?

Total:

Quiz 4   Date: ...... / ...... / ......

1) If the normal distance of a force from a pivot is increased, is it harder or easier to lift a load?

2) How do you find the direction of a resultant force from a scale drawing?

3) Describe the energy transfers that take place when work is done by a force to move an object from one point to another.

4) What variable, other than force, does the moment of a force depend on?

5) What does the direction of a vector arrow tell you about a vector quantity?

6) Is friction a contact force or a non-contact force?

7) What is power?

8) What name is given to the force that can replace all the forces acting on an object, to give the same effect as all the original forces acting together?

9) What are gears used for?

10) What is a free body force diagram?

Total:

Current and Circuits

Current

ELECTRIC CURRENT —
the rate of flow of   .

current

$Q = t$

(coulombs, C)

(   )

(s)

In   , current is caused by   .

Current in Circuits

no source of   source of

(battery)

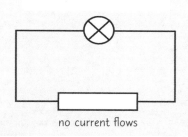

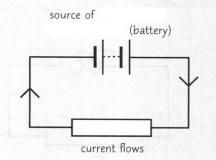

no current flows   current flows

Current through Components

potential difference

(   ) $V = IR$

(amperes, A)

(ohms, Ω)

Resistance is anything that .... the flow of ....

Current through a component depends on the component's
and the   across the component.
The greater the   , the   the current (at a fixed p.d.).
Use a variable resistor to change the   in a circuit:

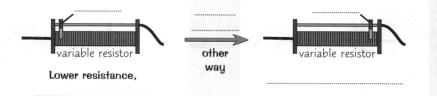

variable resistor

Lower resistance,

....

other
way

variable resistor

....

....

Current and Circuits

Current

ELECTRIC CURRENT —

$$Q =$$

time (s)

In metals,

Current in Circuits

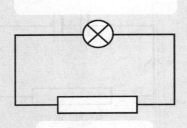

source of

Current through Components

resistance

Resistance is ....

Current through a component

The greater

:

contact

variable resistor

contact

variable resistor

Potential Difference & Circuit Symbols

Potential Difference

POTENTIAL DIFFERENCE —
the energy transferred
_____
that passes between
_____
.

Potential difference can
also be called ....

Energy, Charge and P.d. Equation

(J)

(C)

$$E = QV$$ —— potential
difference ( )

1 volt ( ) = 1 .... (J/C)

Circuit Symbols

....

Battery

....

closed

Voltmeter

Ammeter

Switch

....

Variable resistor

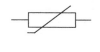

....

....

Diode

LDR (Light-
Dependent Resistor)

....

LED (.....................
....................)

....

Components are connected
by .... —
they represent the wires.

Potential Difference & Circuit Symbols

Potential Difference

POTENTIAL DIFFERENCE —

Energy, Charge and P.d. Equation

Energy
transferred (J)

(J/C)

Circuit Symbols

....

....

open

....

A

....

....

Resistor

....

....

LDR (Light-
Dependent Resistor)

....

....

LED (Light-
Emitting Diode)

....

Components are connected by
....
....
....

Components of Circuits

Three Different Current-Potential Difference Graphs

1 A .... at .... constant temperature

Current is ....
to potential difference...

... so resistance ....

.

‒‒ This graph is .... ‒‒

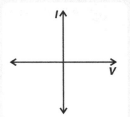

Components with changing resistance (when current through them varies):

2 Filament lamp

Current increases...

... so ....
of filament
increases...

... so resistance ....

.

3 Diode

.... in one direction...

... so current ....

.

‒‒ These graphs are .... ‒‒

LDRs and Thermistors

	LDR	Thermistor
.... depends on...	light intensity	temperature
Lower resistance in...		
Resistance graphs...		(Resistance vs Temperature graph: cold to hot)

Components of Circuits

Three Different Current-Potential Difference Graphs

1 A fixed resistor at

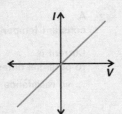

Components with _____ :

2 Filament lamp —⊗—

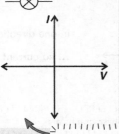

3 Diode —▷|—

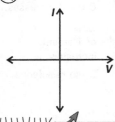

LDRs and Thermistors

	LDR	Thermistor
_____ depends on...		
Lower resistance in...		
Resistance graphs...		

Section 5 — Electricity and Circuits

Mixed Practice Quizzes

Here are some quick-fire quiz questions to test what you've done on p.93-98.
No — don't mention it. Mark each test yourself and tot up your score.

Quiz 1   Date: ...... / ...... / ......

1) What particles make up electric current in a metal?

2) What does the circuit symbol '—⊗—' represent?

3) How does decreasing resistance in a circuit affect the current?

4) What is the circuit symbol for a variable resistor?

5) What is the shape of a current-potential difference graph
   for a fixed resistor at a constant temperature?

6) True or false? Potential difference is measured in volts.

7) What happens to the resistance of an LDR when light intensity increases?

8) What unit is equal to 1 joule per coulomb?

9) What is the equation that links charge, current and time?

10) What is the circuit symbol for a battery?

Total:

Quiz 2   Date: ...... / ...... / ......

1) What is the circuit symbol for a motor?

2) What electrical property is measured in amperes?

3) What is defined as the energy transferred per unit of charge
   that passes between two points in a circuit?

4) Describe the current-potential difference graph for a diode.

5) What is the equation that links potential difference,
   current and resistance?

6) What does the circuit symbol '—Ⓥ—' represent?

7) What does the resistance of a thermistor depend on?

8) True or false? Electric current in a metal is the flow of electrons.

9) What must be included in a circuit in order for current to flow?

10) What is the circuit symbol for a cell?

Total:

Mixed Practice Quizzes

Quiz 3   Date: ...... / ...... / ......

1) What does the circuit symbol '—o——o—' represent?

2) True or false? The current-potential difference graph of a filament lamp is a straight line through the origin.

3) What is the circuit symbol for an LDR?

4) What property is measured in coulombs?

5) What is defined as the rate of flow of charge?

6) What will happen to the current through a component if its resistance increases while the potential difference across it stays the same?

7) What is the equation that links energy transferred, charge moved and potential difference?

8) True or false? In a fixed resistor at a constant temperature, current is inversely proportional to potential difference.

9) What is the circuit symbol for an ammeter?

10) Name the device whose resistance decreases as the light on it gets brighter.

Total:

Quiz 4   Date: ...... / ...... / ......

1) Name two circuit devices whose resistance changes when the current through them changes.

2) What is electric current?

3) What is the circuit symbol for a thermistor?

4) Describe how a variable resistor can be used to change the current in a circuit.

5) What electrical device has a current-potential difference graph that is a straight line through the origin?

6) What are the units of resistance?

7) What is the circuit symbol for a diode?

8) What does the circuit symbol '—⊕—' represent?

9) True or false? 1 ampere equals 1 joule per coulomb.

10) Describe the current-potential difference graph of a filament lamp.

Total:

Section 5 — Electricity and Circuits

Series and Parallel Circuits

Series Circuits

Each component is connected in a line,   with power source.

Current is   .

$$I_1 =$$

Total source potential difference is

$$V_{total} =$$

Total resistance of components
=

$$R_{total} =$$

Adding a resistor in series
.... the total resistance of the circuit.

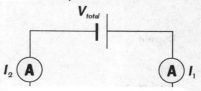

If one component breaks, ...
.... flows in circuit.

Parallel Circuits

Each component is separately connected
on a .... of the circuit.

Total current flowing around a circuit =

$$I_{total} =$$

The total current entering a junction
.... the total current leaving the junction.

Potential difference across each
branch is the same as   .

$$V_1 = V_2 =$$

The total resistance of resistors in parallel
is less than

....

Adding a resistor in parallel
.... the total resistance of the circuit.

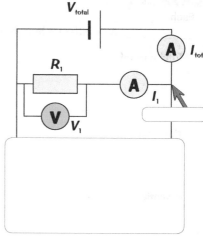

If a component on ....
breaks, components on other
branches .... as current
.... through them.

Section 5 — Electricity and Circuits

Series and Parallel Circuits

Series Circuits

Each _____ is connected in a _____,
_____.

Current _____ = _____

Total source
_____

_____ = _____

Total resistance
_____

_____ = _____

Adding a resistor in series _____.

Parallel Circuits

Each _____
_____ on a different branch of the circuit.

Total current
_____

_____ = _____

The total current
_____

Potential difference
_____

_____ = _____ = _____

The total resistance of resistors in parallel is

Adding a resistor in parallel

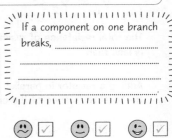

If a component on one branch breaks, _____
_____
_____

Energy and Power in Circuits

Energy Transfers

When charge flows, ... (and so energy is transferred).

 Energy transferred ....

to .... of the
heating element inside the kettle.

 Energy transferred ....

to .... of the fan's motor.

Dissipated Energy in Circuits

Some energy is dissipated to .... when a current
does work .... This has a heating effect.

Current
flows → .... → Ions vibrate more, so → The
through a   the lattice   energy   resistor
resistor   of ions in the resistor

Advantage of heating effect —
e.g. used in   , toasters, etc.
Disadvantage of heating effect —
e.g. causes   .

.... wires used to reduce energy
losses in circuits.

Energy and Power

POWER —

$$P = \frac{E}{t}$$

(watt, W)   time taken (s)

A power rating of an appliance is the

.... between stores per
second when the appliance is in use.

Calculating Power

The
.... or potential difference across a device,
the .... its power.

$$P = IV$$

(W)   (A)

potential
difference (V)

$$P = I^2R$$

(W)   (A)

(Ω)

Second Go:
...... /...... /......

Energy and Power in Circuits

Energy Transfers

When .... flows, ...
(and so ....).

....
to thermal energy store ....
....

....
to kinetic energy store ....

Dissipated Energy in Circuits

Some energy .... when a
current does .... This has a ....

Electrons collide with,	Ions vibrate more, so

Advantage of .... —
e.g. used in .... , ... , etc.
Disadvantage of .... —
e.g. causes ....

Energy and Power

POWER —

$$P = \frac{E}{t}$$

A power rating of an appliance is the

Calculating Power

The higher the current through or

a device, the

current (A)

$$P =$$

 ☑ ☑ ☑

Electricity at Home

Two Types of Electricity Supply

1 _____ — current where movement of charge constantly changes direction.

Produced by _____ , where the positive and negative ends of the potential difference keep alternating. Used in _____ .

2 _____ — current where movement of charge is only in one direction.

Produced by _____ , where the potential difference is only positive or negative, not both.

Supplied by _____ .

Three Facts about UK Mains Supply

1 _____ supply

2 frequency of _____

3 voltage around _____

Three-core Cables

	live wire	neutral wire	_____ wire
Function	_____ from mains supply.		Safety — stops appliance casing becoming live.

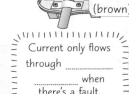

_____ (green and yellow)

_____ (blue)

live (brown)

Current only flows through _____ when there's a fault.

- Potential difference between _____ and _____ = 230 V.
- Potential difference between neutral and earth wire = _____ .

Electric Shocks and Safety

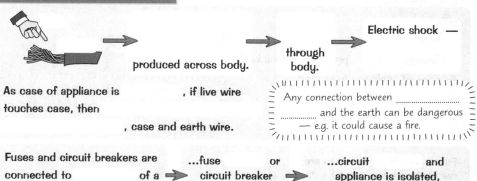

_____ produced across body. → _____ through body. → Electric shock — _____

As case of appliance is _____ , if live wire touches case, then _____ , case and earth wire.

Any connection between _____ _____ and the earth can be dangerous — e.g. it could cause a fire.

Fuses and circuit breakers are connected to _____ of a device, so if current surges... → ...fuse _____ or circuit breaker _____ ... → ...circuit _____ and appliance is isolated, preventing _____ .

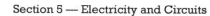

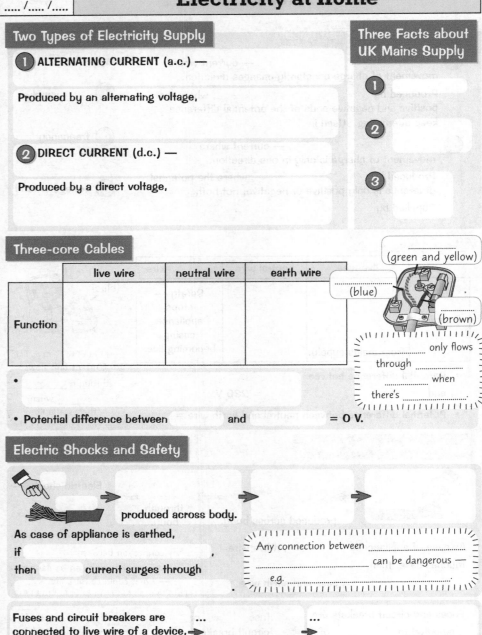

Electricity at Home

Two Types of Electricity Supply

1 ALTERNATING CURRENT (a.c.) —

Produced by an alternating voltage,

2 DIRECT CURRENT (d.c.) —

Produced by a direct voltage,

Three Facts about UK Mains Supply

1

2

3

Three-core Cables

	live wire	neutral wire	earth wire
Function			

....
(green and yellow)

....
(blue)

....
(brown)

.... only flows
through ....
.... when
there's ....

• ....

• Potential difference between .... and .... = 0 V.

Electric Shocks and Safety

.... produced across body.

As case of appliance is earthed,

if ....,

then .... current surges through

....

Any connection between ....
.... can be dangerous —
e.g. ....

Fuses and circuit breakers are
connected to live wire of a device, → ... → ...

...   ...

Mixed Practice Quizzes

I hope you're not too frazzled from pages 101-106, because it's time for you to try some quiz questions. Give them a go, mark your test, and see how you did.

Quiz 1   Date: ...... / ...... / ......

1) What is meant by alternating current?
2) What happens to the total resistance of a circuit when another resistor is added to the circuit in series?
3) What electrical property is the same on every branch of a parallel circuit?
4) What type of current is supplied by a cell?
5) What happens when a circuit breaker connected to a device trips?
6) What is meant by the power rating of a device?
7) True or false? A connection between a live wire and the earth can cause a fire.
8) What is the size of the voltage of the UK mains supply?
9) What is the purpose of the earth wire in a three-core cable?
10) What do electrons collide with when current flows through a resistor?

Total:

Quiz 2   Date: ...... / ...... / ......

1) What electrical property is the same everywhere in a series circuit?
2) What happens when a very high current passes through a fuse?
3) True or false? The UK mains supply provides direct current.
4) What is the potential difference between the live wire and the earth wire for an appliance connected to the mains?
5) Describe one energy transfer that occurs when an electric kettle is used.
6) True or false? The total resistance of two resistors in parallel is less than the resistance of the smaller of the two resistors.
7) What is the equation that links power, energy transferred and time taken?
8) Give one difference between series and parallel circuits.
9) State the equation that links electrical power, current and resistance.
10) When a current flows through a resistor, what happens to its temperature?

Total:

Mixed Practice Quizzes

Quiz 3   Date: ...... / ...... / ......

1) True or false? The earth wire only carries current if there is a fault.

2) How do you calculate the total resistance
   of two resistors connected in series?

3) What type of current is supplied by the UK mains supply?

4) During an electric shock, what happens after
   a large potential difference is produced across the body?

5) What type of voltage produces direct current?

6) What is the potential difference between the neutral wire and the earth wire?

7) True or false? The power of an appliance decreases
   if the potential difference across it increases.

8) What causes some energy to be dissipated to thermal energy stores
   when a current flows?

9) What is defined as the energy transferred per second?

10) Give one advantage of the heating effect of electric current.

Total:

Quiz 4   Date: ...... / ...... / ......

1) In what type of circuit is the current the same at every point in the circuit?

2) Give one disadvantage of the heating effect of electric current.

3) What is the frequency of the UK mains supply?

4) State the equation that links power, potential difference and current.

5) How does adding a resistor in parallel affect the total resistance of a circuit?

6) In what type of current is the motion of charge
   constantly changing direction?

7) What wire of a three-core cable is a fuse connected to?

8) True or false? The total current entering a junction
   is equal to the total current leaving the junction.

9) Why are low resistance wires used in circuits?

10) What is the purpose of the live wire in a three-core cable?

Total:

Electric Fields

Electric Fields Around A Point Charge

ELECTRIC FIELD — a region in which .... feels a ....

An electric field is created around any .... object.

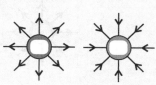

Strong electric fields .... air particles, which can cause ....

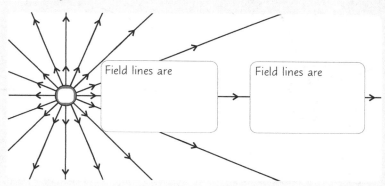

Field lines are

Field lines are

Electric Fields Between Parallel Plates

The electric field between two .... is uniform.

Equally spaced field lines — .... is the same everywhere.

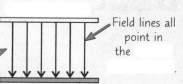

Field lines all point in the ....

Attraction and Repulsion of Charges

When a charged object is placed in the .... of another charged object, they ....

.... :

.... :

Electric Fields

Electric Fields Around A Point Charge

ELECTRIC FIELD —

An electric field is

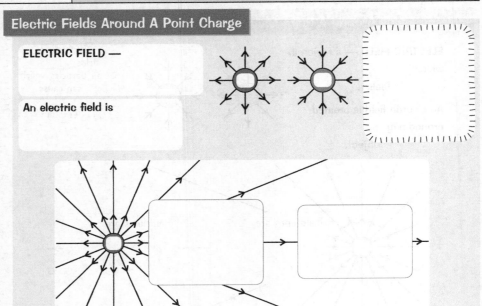

Electric Fields Between Parallel Plates

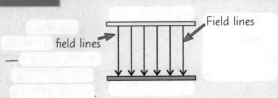

field lines

Field lines

Attraction and Repulsion of Charges

When a charged object

:   :

Static Electricity

Static Charging by Friction

Rub two .... together.

⬇

.... move from one to the other.

⬇

Both materials become .... Charge on each material is ....

Only .... move, ... don't move.

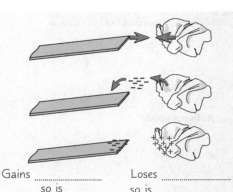

Gains .... so is .... charged.

Loses .... so is .... charged.

Sparks and Earthing

Electric charge ...

... . between object and earth ...

...when .... is large enough, ... (a spark).

Examples of sparking:

Objects are earthed to ....

Earthing provides a connection ....

Attraction by Induction

Static charge ....

Balloon ....
and attracted to opposite charges on ....

uncharged wall

Same effect causes ....
.... toward a charged comb.

Electrostatic Sprayers

Each drop has the ....

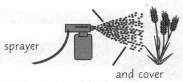

sprayer

.... and cover

crops with a ....

Dangers

Static charge can build up while .... A spark could ....

Fuel tanks are ....

Section 6 — Electric and Magnetic Fields

Static Electricity

Static Charging by Friction

Both materials

Sparks and Earthing

Electric

...p.d.

...when p.d.

Examples of sparking:

Objects are   .

Attraction by Induction

Balloon

Same effect causes paper scraps to ....

Electrostatic Sprayers

Each drop

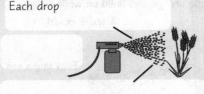

Dangers

Static charge

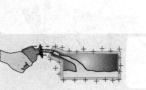

Magnets

Magnetic Fields

PERMANENT MAGNET —

MAGNETIC FIELD — region where other .... experience a force.

Magnetic field is .... at the poles.

Magnetic field strength .... with .... distance from magnet.

Field is .... where field lines are closer together.

Field lines show .... force would act on a ...., if placed at that point.

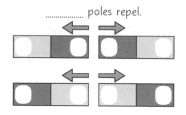

Forces between magnets are due to their ....

Magnetic Repulsion

.... poles repel.

Magnetic Attraction

.... poles attract.

Uniform magnetic field between .... poles — .... (strength same everywhere) and in ....

Induced Magnets and Magnetic Materials

INDUCED MAGNET — a .... that only produces a magnetic field when it's ....

permanent magnet | induced magnet

N S | N S

A permanent magnet and an induced magnet are always .... to each other.

When the induced magnet is moved away from the permanent magnet, it ....

Four magnetic materials:

1 iron 2 .... 3 nickel 4 ....

Uses of Magnets

• ....

• Separating ....

• Maglev trains

• ....

Magnets

Magnetic Fields

PERMANENT MAGNET —

MAGNETIC FIELD —

Magnetic field is

Field is

Magnetic field strength

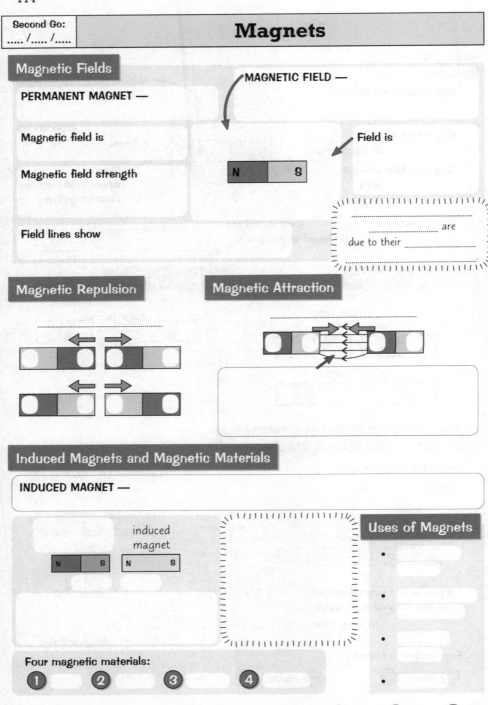

N   S

Field lines show

.... are
due to their ....

Magnetic Repulsion

Magnetic Attraction

Induced Magnets and Magnetic Materials

INDUCED MAGNET —

induced
magnet

N   S   N   S

Uses of Magnets

•

•

•

•

Four magnetic materials:

1   2   3   4

Section 6 — Electric and Magnetic Fields

Compasses and the Motor Effect

Compasses

Compass needle points in the direction of

A compass needle is

Place a compass at different positions in a to show its

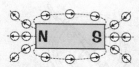

When a compass isn't near a magnet, its needle points . This is because Earth

(Earth's core is magnetic).

Current-Carrying Conductor

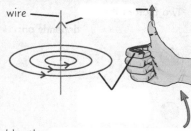

wire

Use the
to work out direction of field.

Two factors the magnetic field strength depends on:

1 Size of .
Larger current, field.

2 the conductor.

Force on a Conductor

MOTOR EFFECT — when a magnet and conductor exert

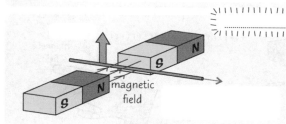

magnetic field

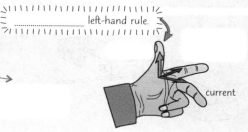

left-hand rule.

current

Compasses and the Motor Effect

Compasses

Place a compass at

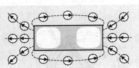

Current-Carrying Conductor

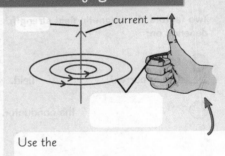

current

Use the

Two factors the

depends on:

1

2

Force on a Conductor

MOTOR EFFECT —

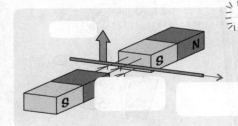

magnetic
field

Section 6 — Electric and Magnetic Fields

Mixed Practice Quizzes

Now you've charged yourself up with knowledge, give these quiz questions on pages 109-116 a go. Let's see if your brain's sparking in the right way...

Quiz 1   Date: ...... / ...... / ......

1) True or false? A compass needle points in the direction of the magnetic field it's in.
2) What is an electric field?
3) Name two magnetic materials.
4) Where is the magnetic field of a bar magnet strongest?
5) Describe the motor effect.
6) Describe the forces that act between two positively charged objects.
7) What is a permanent magnet?
8) True or false? Static charge is caused by the movement of positive charges.
9) In Fleming's left-hand rule, which digit shows the direction of the current?
10) What is the name for the passage of electrons across a gap between a charged object and the earth?

Total:

Quiz 2   Date: ...... / ...... / ......

1) Describe the force between two magnets when their south poles are brought close to each other.
2) In electrostatic sprayers, how does static charge ensure a fine, even spray?
3) What is a magnetic field?
4) In Fleming's left-hand rule, what does the thumb show the direction of?
5) True or false? A cobalt rod cannot become an induced magnet.
6) Describe the electric field between two oppositely charged parallel plates.
7) How are static charges formed when insulating materials rub together?
8) Describe what a compass will show when placed in a magnetic field.
9) True or false? The stronger an electric field, the further apart its field lines.
10) Describe the magnetic field shape around a straight current-carrying wire.

Total:

Mixed Practice Quizzes

Quiz 3   Date: ...... / ...... / ......

1) What two factors affect the magnetic field strength around a current-carrying wire?

2) How is a positive static charge formed?

3) How does magnetic field strength change with distance from a magnet?

4) True or false? The attraction between a charged comb and scraps of paper is due to induced charge.

5) Do electric field lines point towards or away from a negative point charge?

6) Give two uses of magnets.

7) What is an electric spark?

8) Why is it important that fuel tanks are earthed?

9) True or false? The electric field between two oppositely charged parallel plates is uniform.

10) What causes a compass needle to point north when it's not near a magnet?

Total:

Quiz 4   Date: ...... / ...... / ......

1) True or false? Strong electric fields can ionise air, causing a spark.

2) How could you find the direction of the magnetic field around a long current-carrying conductor?

3) What type of static charge is formed when an object gains electrons?

4) True or false? Unlike electric charges will repel each other.

5) Describe the magnetic field between two opposite poles of a magnet.

6) Which pole do magnetic field lines point towards?

7) What happens to the magnetic field of an induced magnet when it is removed from an external magnetic field?

8) How does earthing allow static charges to be discharged?

9) In Fleming's left-hand rule, which digit shows the direction of the magnetic field?

10) Why does a statically charged balloon stick to a wall?

Total:

Motors, Solenoids and Induced P.d.

Electric Motors

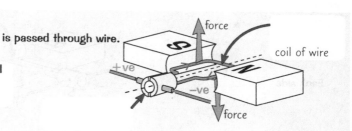

is passed through wire.

↓

Each side of the coil

↓

Coil rotates.

force

coil of wire

+ve

−ve

force

Solenoids

SOLENOID — a long cylindrical ....

Inside solenoid, magnetic fields of each turn of wire
to form

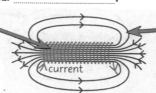

current

> A solenoid is an example of
> an ....

Outside solenoid, magnetic fields cancel to

.... , which
is same shape as a

Electromagnetic Induction

ELECTROMAGNETIC INDUCTION — the .... (and current if there's
a complete circuit) in a wire which is experiencing a ....

Two ways to induce a ...	①	②
To swap the direction of the ...	Move the wire in . or Start with both magnets .	Move the magnet in . or Start with the magnet .
To increase the size of the induced ...	Increase the . or Increase the .	For a coil, can also increase ....

An induced current generates its own ....

This .... always acts .... the change that made it.

Motors, Solenoids and Induced P.d.

Electric Motors

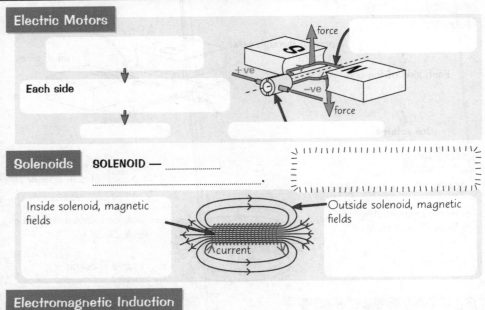

Each side

force

+ve

−ve

force

Solenoids

SOLENOID — ....
....

Inside solenoid, magnetic
fields

Outside solenoid, magnetic
fields

current

Electromagnetic Induction

ELECTROMAGNETIC INDUCTION — ....
....
....

Two ways to induce a	①	②
To swap the direction of the	or	or
To increase the size of the induced	or	For a ...., can also ....

An induced current ....
This ....

Generators & Electromagnetic Devices

Alternators

Alternators generate _____ .

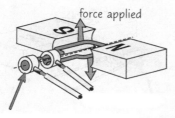

force applied

_____ prevent contacts from swapping as it turns

Dynamos

Dynamos generate _____ .

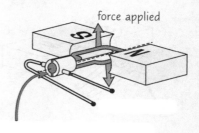

force applied

_____ swaps contacts each half turn

Loudspeakers and Headphones

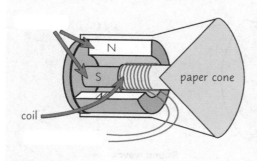

N

S

coil

paper cone

_____ is sent through coil.

↓

Coil _____ .

↓

Paper cone moves back and forth.

↓

_____ are created.

Microphones

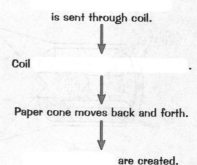

N

S

coil

_____ hit diaphragm.

↓

Diaphragm moves _____ .

↓

_____ moves back and forth.

↓

_____ is generated.

Section 6 — Electric and Magnetic Fields

Generators & Electromagnetic Devices

Alternators

Alternators generate

[_____] .

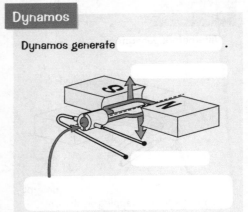

Dynamos

Dynamos generate [_____] .

Loudspeakers and Headphones

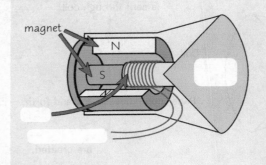

magnet

N

S

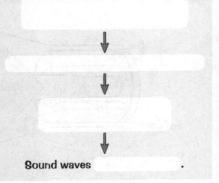

[_____]

↓

[_____]

↓

[_____]

↓

Sound waves [_____] .

Microphones

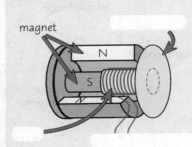

magnet

N

S

Sound waves [_____] .

↓

[_____]

↓

[_____]

↓

[_____]

 ☑ ☑ ☑

Transformers and the National Grid

Transformers

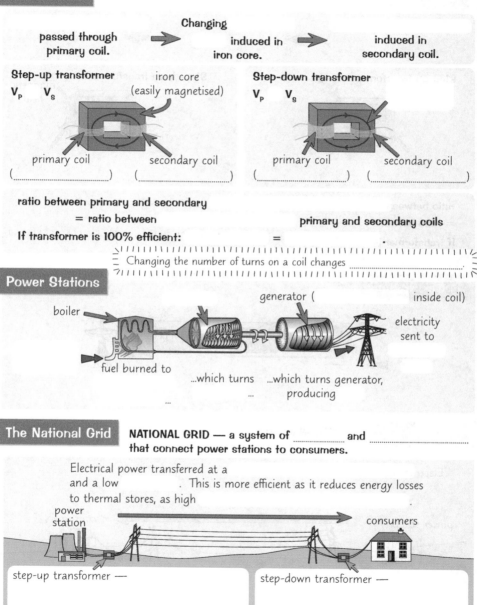

Changing

passed through primary coil. ⟶ induced in iron core. ⟶ induced in secondary coil.

Step-up transformer V_p V_s — iron core (easily magnetised)

Step-down transformer V_p V_s

primary coil (..............) secondary coil (..............)

primary coil (..............) secondary coil (..............)

ratio between primary and secondary
= ratio between .... primary and secondary coils

If transformer is 100% efficient: =   .

Changing the number of turns on a coil changes ....

Power Stations

generator (........... inside coil)

boiler

electricity sent to

fuel burned to ...

...which turns ...which turns generator, producing ...

The National Grid

NATIONAL GRID — a system of .... and .... that connect power stations to consumers.

Electrical power transferred at a .... and a low .... This is more efficient as it reduces energy losses to thermal stores, as high ....

power station

consumers

step-up transformer —

step-down transformer —

Section 6 — Electric and Magnetic Fields

Transformers and the National Grid

Transformers

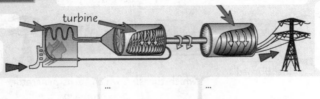

Step-up transformer

Step-down transformer

magnetic field

ratio between
= ratio between

If transformer is

: ═══════════════
=

Power Stations

turbine

...   ...

...   ...

The National Grid

NATIONAL GRID —

Electrical power

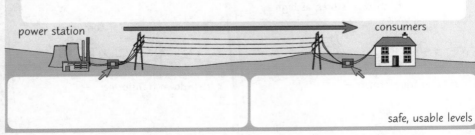

power station

consumers

safe, usable levels

Mixed Practice Quizzes

Keep that motor turning, it's time for some quick quiz questions on pages 119-124. Time to see if you can transform your revision into the correct answers...

Quiz 1   Date: ...... / ...... / ......

1) What type of generator produces direct current?

2) What type of transformer has a higher potential difference across its secondary coil than across its primary coil?

3) Give one way to reverse the direction of an induced potential difference that was caused by moving a wire inside a magnetic field.

4) What is the national grid?

5) Describe how a simple electric motor works.

6) True or false? A solenoid is an example of an electromagnet.

7) Name a device that converts alternating current into sound waves.

8) Explain why step-up transformers are used in the national grid.

9) What is an alternator?

10) True or false? In power stations, fuel is burnt to heat a generator.

Total:

Quiz 2   Date: ...... / ...... / ......

1) What device is used to decrease the potential difference of the electricity supply in the national grid?

2) How can you increase the size of an induced potential difference?

3) What type of generator produces alternating current?

4) Name a material used for the core of a transformer.

5) For what kind of transformer is $V_p > V_s$ true?

6) True or false? Microphones produce direct current from sound waves.

7) Why is transferring electricity at high current inefficient?

8) How is the number of turns on a transformer's coils related to the input and output potential differences?

9) True or false? The magnetic field outside a solenoid is strong and uniform.

10) What type of generator includes a split-ring commutator?

Total:

Mixed Practice Quizzes

Quiz 3   Date: ...... / ...... / ......

1) Which coil has more turns in a step-down transformer?

2) True or false? An induced current will generate a magnetic field that opposes the change that made it.

3) Describe how a simple transformer works.

4) How does the strength of a magnetic field affect the size of an induced potential difference?

5) Describe and explain the magnetic field inside a solenoid.

6) What type of current is generated by a dynamo?

7) Why is electricity transferred through the national grid with a low current?

8) Describe how loudspeakers produce sound waves from alternating current.

9) What must be true if a transformer's output power equals its input power?

10) True or false? There is no change to the potential difference when electricity is transmitted from the power station to the consumer.

Total:

Quiz 4   Date: ...... / ...... / ......

1) Name the system of cables and transformers that connects power stations to consumers.

2) Describe how electricity is generated in power stations.

3) True or false? Moving a magnet in and out of a coil of wire will induce a potential difference across the coil.

4) Explain why step-down transformers are used in the national grid.

5) What type of generator contains slip rings and brushes?

6) For what kind of transformer is $V_s > V_p$ true?

7) Describe how electricity gets from power stations to the consumer.

8) Describe and explain the magnetic field outside a solenoid.

9) In electromagnetic induction, how does increasing the speed of movement affect the size of the p.d. induced?

10) What device converts sound waves into alternating current?

Total:

Density and The Particle Model

Density

DENSITY —

$$\rho = \frac{m}{V}$$

mass (kg)

volume (   )

States of Matter

	Particle arrangement	Forces between particles	Distance between particles	Particle motion
SOLID		Strong		Vibration only
LIQUID	Irregular	Weak		
GAS			Large	

Density

Changes of State

Changes of state are   .   is always conserved.

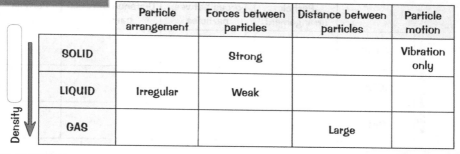

melt

sublimate

or evaporate

gas

....
....
.... during a
change of state.

Physical and Chemical Changes

PHYSICAL CHANGE — same substance in a
.
If you reverse the change, substance

.

CHEMICAL CHANGE —
new substance   .

Heating

Heating transfers   to a substance.
This can do one of two things:

1 Increase the   —
Energy transferred to   energy stores
of substance's   (more energy in
these stores =   ).

2 Change the   —
Energy used to   .

Density and The Particle Model

Density

DENSITY —

density (kg/m³)

States of Matter

	Particle arrangement	Forces between particles	Distance between particles	Particle motion
SOLID				
LIQUID				
GAS				

Changes of State

Changes of state ....
....

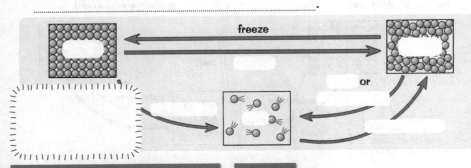

freeze

or

Physical and Chemical Changes

PHYSICAL CHANGE —

CHEMICAL CHANGE —

Heating

.... to a
substance. This can do one of two things:

1 —
Energy transferred

2 —

Heating, Temperature and Pressure

Specific Heat Capacity and Specific Latent Heat

SPECIFIC HEAT CAPACITY — the amount of energy needed to raise

.

SPECIFIC LATENT HEAT — the amount of energy needed to change

, without changing

.

SPECIFIC LATENT HEAT OF   — the specific
latent heat of changing between a solid   .
SPECIFIC LATENT HEAT OF VAPORISATION — the specific
latent heat of changing

.

Absolute Zero

Converting between
kelvin and Celsius:

Celsius   kelvin

ABSOLUTE ZERO — 0 K, or   .
The temperature at which particles
have

in their
— they're almost still.

Absolute zero is the ....
....

Gas Pressure

Gas particles are

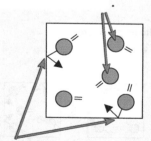

When particles   with a surface...

... they
and so a   pressure.

A Gas at Constant Volume

Temperature

Particles get faster and
collide with the container

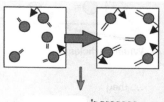

increases

Second Go:
...... / ...... / ......

Heating, Temperature and Pressure

Specific Heat Capacity and Specific Latent Heat

SPECIFIC HEAT CAPACITY —

SPECIFIC LATENT HEAT —

↘ **SPECIFIC LATENT HEAT OF FUSION —** ....
....

SPECIFIC LATENT HEAT OF VAPORISATION — ....
....

Absolute Zero

Converting between kelvin and Celsius:

ABSOLUTE ZERO —

Gas Pressure

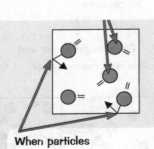

When particles

... they

A Gas at Constant Volume

Particles get faster

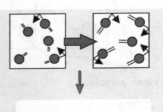

Pressure and Work on Gases

Net Force from Gas Pressure

All the

with a surface add to

on

that surface.

Net force acts

to the surface.

Pressure Changes

For a gas inside a container that can change   (e.g. a balloon),

:

pressure outside > pressure inside

gas ....

pressure outside < pressure inside

gas ....

A Gas at Constant Temperature

Volume increases

Particles   and collide with the container   .

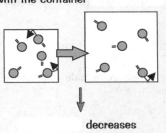

decreases

Doing Work on Gases

is applied to gas.   on the gas
increases the energy in   of an enclosed gas
as
energy is transferred.   .

.... is applied to
air in ....
....   Energy in ....
                    increases in tyre.   Tyre temperature
....

Section 7 — Matter

Pressure and Work on Gases

Net Force from Gas Pressure

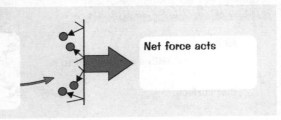

Net force acts

Pressure Changes

For a gas inside a container

pressure outside   pressure inside

pressure outside   pressure inside

A Gas at Constant Temperature

Volume

Doing Work on Gases

Doing work

in bike pump and tyre.

Tyre temperature

Elasticity

Changing Shape

_____ to act on a stationary object to change its shape.

stretch

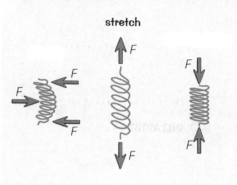

Two Types of Distortion

1. **ELASTIC** — object goes back to

   _____ after forces have been removed.

   Elastic objects can be
   ....
   ....

2. **INELASTIC** — object doesn't go back to

   _____ .

Force-Extension Relationship for an Elastic Object

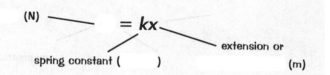

$$\text{(N)} \underline{\quad\quad} = kx$$

spring constant ( )   extension or _____ (m)

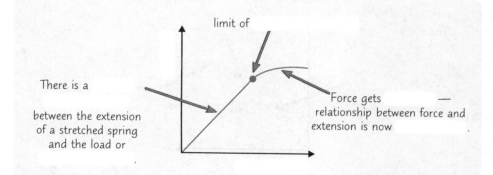

limit of

There is a

between the extension of a stretched spring and the load or

Force gets _____ — relationship between force and extension is now _____ .

Second Go:
....../....../......

Elasticity

Changing Shape

More than one ....

....

....

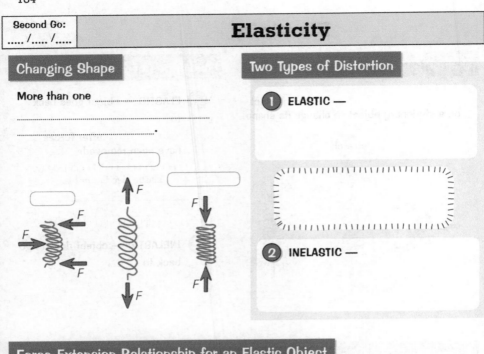

Two Types of Distortion

1 ELASTIC —

2 INELASTIC —

Force-Extension Relationship for an Elastic Object

or compression (m)

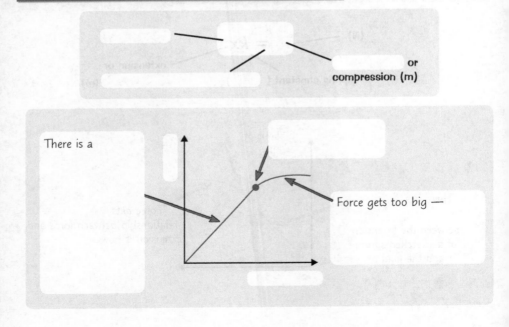

There is a

Force gets too big —

Fluid Pressure and Upthrust

Pressure

pressure (   )   force
             to a surface (N)

$$p = \frac{F}{A}$$

of that
surface (   )

High-heeled shoes

Smaller .... =
.... pressure

Snowshoes

Larger .... =
.... pressure

Pressure of a
a force is
surface

(a liquid or gas) means
to any
.

Pressure Differences in a Fluid

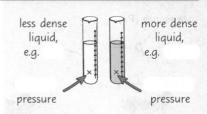

less dense
liquid,
e.g.

more dense
liquid,
e.g.

pressure   pressure

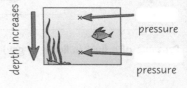

depth increases

pressure

pressure

Upthrust

UPTHRUST — the
on an object submerged in liquid, due to the   of the
liquid being greater at the   of the object than at the   .

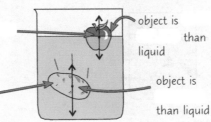

so object floats

object is
            than
liquid

object is

so object sinks

than liquid

Upthrust is equal
to weight of liquid
that has been
....

Atmospheric Pressure

THE ATMOSPHERE —

that surrounds the Earth.

Atmospheric pressure is created
on a surface by   .

above Earth ➡
increases.

Number of
decreases
and
of air above
a surface decreases.

➡ **Atmospheric
pressure**

atmospheric
pressure

atmospheric
pressure

Atmosphere gets .... as height increases.

 ✓ ✓ ✓

Second Go:
...../...../.....

Fluid Pressure and Upthrust

Pressure

pressure (Pa)

$$p = \dfrac{\quad}{\quad}$$

High-heeled shoes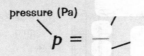

Snowshoes

....
....

....

Pressure of a fluid (a liquid or gas)

Pressure Differences in a Fluid

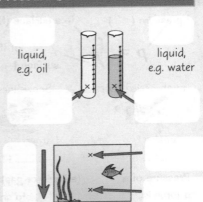

liquid, e.g. oil

liquid, e.g. water

Upthrust

UPTHRUST — the resultant force acting upwards

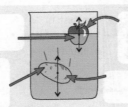

Upthrust is equal to

Atmospheric Pressure

THE ATMOSPHERE —

Atmospheric pressure is

Height above Earth ➡

Number of

Atmospheric pressure

.

Mixed Practice Quizzes

Test yourself on pages 127-136. Deep breath — it's quite literally mind over matter.

Quiz 1   Date: ...... / ...... / ......

1) What is the difference between specific
    heat capacity and specific latent heat?
2) What is meant by upthrust?
3) Explain why atmospheric pressure decreases as height increases.
4) Which state of matter has the biggest distance between its particles?
5) What is meant by the density of a substance?
6) Explain why pumping a tyre with air can cause the tyre to heat up.
7) True or false? Changes of state are chemical changes.
8) What is the equation that links force, spring constant and extension?
9) Describe the arrangement of particles in solids, liquids and gases.
10) Describe the shape of a force-extension graph for an elastic object.

Total:

Quiz 2   Date: ...... / ...... / ......

1) For a given force, how does increasing the area
    over which the force is applied affect the pressure exerted?
2) What should you do to convert a temperature from Celsius to kelvin?
3) The shape of an object can be changed by bending or stretching the
    object. Give one other way that the shape of an object can be changed.
4) In which direction does the net force of gas particles act on a surface?
5) True or false? Mass is always conserved during changes of state.
6) Give the definition for the specific latent heat of vaporisation.
7) Name the term given for a gas turning into a liquid.
8) Describe how pressure changes with the depth of a fluid.
9) True or false? There is always a non-linear relationship between the
    extension of a stretched spring and the force applied to the spring.
10) Explain what happens to the pressure of a gas if you increase
    its volume whilst keeping it at a constant temperature.

Total:

Mixed Practice Quizzes

Quiz 3   Date: ...... / ...... / ......

1) True or false? Heating a substance always increases its temperature. ☑

2) Explain what happens to the pressure of a gas if you increase its temperature whilst keeping it at a constant volume. ☑

3) Which usually has a lower density — a solid or a liquid? ☑

4) What is a spring constant measured in? ☑

5) Describe the difference between a physical change and a chemical change. ☑

6) Between which two states of matter does freezing occur? ☑

7) What causes gas pressure? ☑

8) If work is done on an enclosed gas, what can happen to its temperature? ☑

9) If the upthrust acting on an object is equal to its weight, will the object float or sink? ☑

10) Is the atmospheric pressure higher at the top or the bottom of a mountain? ☑

Total:

Quiz 4   Date: ...... / ...... / ......

1) Describe the difference between elastic distortion and inelastic distortion. ☑

2) What is the equation that links pressure, force and area? ☑

3) True or false? When an object is placed in a liquid, the upthrust is equal to the weight of liquid displaced by the object. ☑

4) True or false? Only one force has to act on a stationary object to change its shape. ☑

5) What happens to the air in an air-filled balloon if the air pressure is greater on the outside of the balloon than on the inside? ☑

6) Describe the motion of particles in a solid. ☑

7) If one liquid has a higher density than another liquid, which liquid will have a higher pressure at a certain depth? ☑

8) Give the formula for density. ☑

9) Describe what is meant by the term 'absolute zero'. ☑

10) Give the definition for the specific latent heat of fusion. ☑

Total:

Core Practicals 1

Two Experiments that Test $F = ma$

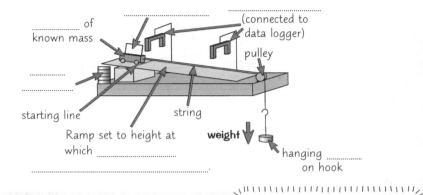

.... of
known mass

.... (connected to
data logger)

pulley

....

....

starting line

string

Ramp set to height at
which ....

weight ↓

hanging ....
on hook

....

1　Investigate effect of

- Add　　　　　to　　.

- 　　　　trolley from　　.
　　　record trolley's acceleration.

- Add another　　to trolley and repeat until　　.

Increasing

acceleration.

Each light gate measures ....
and .... when trolley
passes through.
.... is found from
change in ....
÷ ....

Independent Variable	Dependent Variable	Control Variable
	acceleration	

2　Investigate effect of

- Start with　　　　　.

- Release　　from　　.
　Light gates record trolley's　　.

- Move　　from　　to hook and repeat measurement.

- Keep going　　.

Increasing
increases acceleration.

Independent Variable	Dependent Variable	Control Variable
		mass

Second Go:
..... / ..... / .....

Core Practicals 1

Two Experiments that Test $F = ma$

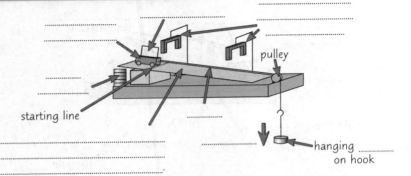

....

....

pulley

starting line

....

....
....
....

hanging ....
on hook

---

1 Investigate effect of ....

- **Add**

- **Release**

- **Add another**

Increasing

Each light gate measures ....
....
....

Acceleration is ....
....

Independent Variable	
Dependent Variable	
Control Variable	

---

2 Investigate effect of ....

- **Start with**

- **Release**

- **Move a**

- **Keep going**

Increasing

Independent Variable	
Dependent Variable	
Control Variable	

Core Practicals

Core Practicals 2

Measuring Properties of Three Different Waves

1 Waves in air.

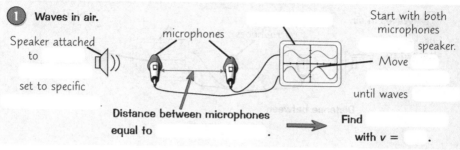

Speaker attached to

set to specific

microphones

Start with both microphones

speaker.

Move

until waves

Distance between microphones equal to   .

Find   with $v =$.

2 Waves in a ripple tank.

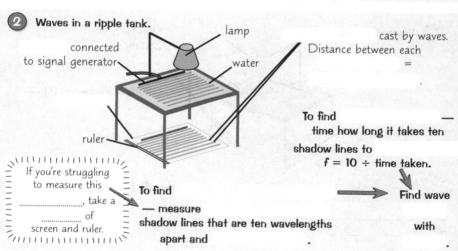

connected to signal generator

lamp

water

ruler

cast by waves.
Distance between each   =

To find   —
time how long it takes ten shadow lines to
$f = 10 ÷$ time taken.

If you're struggling to measure this ...., take a .... of screen and ruler.

To find   — measure   shadow lines that are ten wavelengths apart and   .

Find wave   with

3 Waves in a solid.

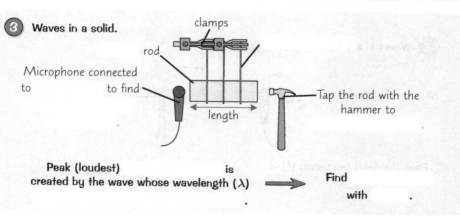

clamps

rod

Microphone connected to   to find

length

Tap the rod with the hammer to

Peak (loudest)   is created by the wave whose wavelength (λ)

Find   with   .

Core Practicals

Core Practicals 2

Measuring Properties of Three Different Waves

1 Waves in air.

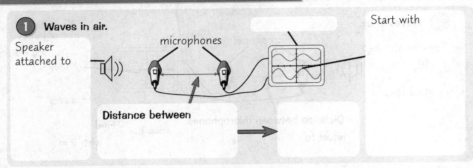

Speaker attached to

microphones

Distance between

Start with

2 Waves in a ripple tank.

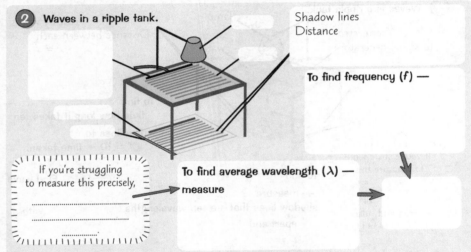

Shadow lines
Distance

To find frequency (f) —

If you're struggling to measure this precisely,
....
....
....

To find average wavelength (λ) —
measure

3 Waves in a solid.

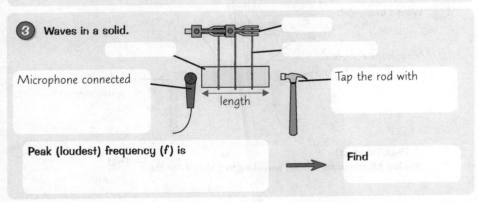

Microphone connected

length

Tap the rod with

Peak (loudest) frequency (f) is

Find

Core Practicals

Core Practicals 3

Four Steps to Investigate Refraction

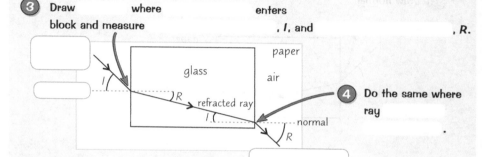

1 Trace around _____ , then trace _____ ray and _____ ray.

2 Remove block and join _____ ray and _____ ray with _____ (refracted ray).

paper

rectangular glass block

_____ ray   _____ ray

3 Draw _____ where _____ enters block and measure _____ , *I*, and _____ , *R*.

glass   paper

air

I

)*R* refracted ray

I

normal

R

4 Do the same where _____ ray _____ .

When the ray enters the block _____ > _____ and when it leaves _____ > _____ . This means:

- Ray bends _____ normal going from air to glass
  — light is _____ in glass than air.
- Ray bends _____ normal going from glass to air
  — light is _____ in air than glass.

Investigating Emission of Radiation

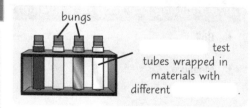

- _____ and fill each test tube with _____ .
- Measure _____ at regular intervals.
  _____ drops _____ if surface a better emitter.
- A _____ surface is a better emitter than a _____ one.
- A _____ surface is a better emitter than a _____ one.

bungs

_____ test tubes wrapped in materials with different _____ .

Independent Variable	_____ surface
Dependent Variable	
Control Variables	e.g. volume of water, shape of test tube

Core Practicals

Core Practicals 3

Four Steps to Investigate Refraction

1. Trace around

2. Remove block and

3. Draw normal

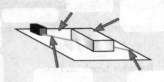

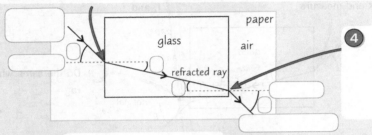

paper

glass

air

4

refracted ray

When the ray _____ . This means:

- Ray _____ going from air to glass
  — light _____ glass than air.

- Ray _____ going from glass to air
  — light _____ air than glass.

Investigating Emission of Radiation

- Boil

- Measure

- A black surface is _____

- A matte surface is _____

Independent Variable	
Dependent Variable	
Control Variables	

Core Practicals 4

Investigating Components and Circuits

Two steps to investigate a single component:

1 Vary _____ of source.

2 Take _____ of readings for _____ .

Plot values on _____ to show _____

relationship between _____ :

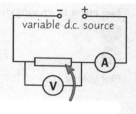

variable d.c. source

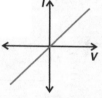

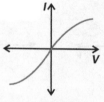

— e.g.
resistor or filament lamp.

Make sure the
circuit doesn't

_____
— disconnect it for a
while if _____
_____ .

Use _____ to work out the resistance for each pair of
measurements to see how it changes _____ .

Investigating series and parallel circuits:

* Using the circuit above, connect a second _____ component either...

...in _____ ... ...or in _____ :

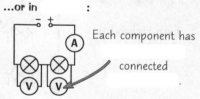

Each branch has a _____ Each component has
_____ ,
an _____ _____ connected
and a _____ .

* Follow _____ for the new circuit — see how _____
for each component and the circuit as a whole.

* You could then add more _____ (in parallel) or more _____ (in series).

You should find:

	Series	Parallel
Increase source p.d.	Total _____ through circuit also increases.	
P.d. across each component	Source p.d. _____ _____ components.	_____ source p.d.
Total current through circuit	Same _____ ' _____ as components added.	_____ current in branches, _____ as components added.

Core Practicals 4

Investigating Components and Circuits

Two steps to investigate a single component:

1

2

Plot values

:

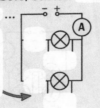

Use

variable d.c. source

— e.g.

or

Make sure ....
....
....
....

Investigating series and parallel circuits:

- Using the circuit above, connect   either...

...   ...

Each branch has

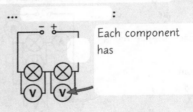

...   :

Each component
has

- Follow

- You could then

You should find:

You should find:	Series	Parallel
Increase source p.d.		
P.d. across each component		Same as ....
Total current through circuit	Same ...., decreases as	

Core Practicals

Core Practicals 5

Determining Density of Solids and Liquids

To measure density of a solid or liquid, find its .... and ...., then use: $\longrightarrow$ density (kg/m³) = ———————

Regular solid

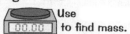 Use .... to find mass. $\longrightarrow$ Measure object. Calculate volume using relevant ....

Irregular solid

mass of object =

object, m_1, m_2, m_3

To find volume:

mass of displaced water = $m_1 + m_2$ –

volume of displaced water = ... of displaced water ÷ .... of water (known)

volume of .... = volume of displaced water

Liquid

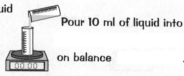 Pour 10 ml of liquid into .... on balance .... $\longrightarrow$ Record .... shown on .... and total .... shown on ....

Investigating Springs

Four steps to find the relationship between force and extension:

1 Measure .... of spring with ruler.

2 Add .... to spring (causing it to ....).

3 Calculate force and extension:

Force = ... of masses =
(m is total mass on ....,

g is ....)

Extension = ... length – .... length

Independent Variable	
Dependent Variable	

4 Add another mass and repeat readings. Plot a graph when ....

clamp
fixed ruler
hanging mass
stand

Force (N) / Extension (m)

Area under linear section =
....
....
....

Core Practicals 5

Determining Density of Solids and Liquids

To measure .... : density (kg/m³) = ——————

....

 solid 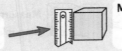 Measure

 solid

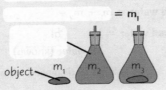

$= m_1$

object m_1 m_2 m_3

To find volume:

mass of displaced water =

volume of displaced water =

volume of object =

 Liquid Pour 10 ml of liquid Record

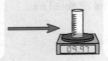

Investigating Springs

Four steps to find the relationship between force and extension:

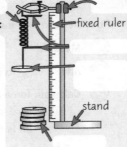 fixed ruler

1 Measure

2 Add

3 Calculate

Force =

Extension =

stand

Independent Variable	
Dependent Variable	

4 Add another mass and

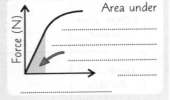

Force (N)

Area under
....
....
....
....

Core Practicals 6

Four Steps to Find the Specific Heat Capacity of Water

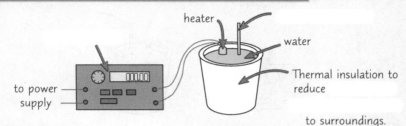

heater

water

Thermal insulation to reduce

to power supply

to surroundings.

1. Fill the container with a .... of water.

2. Measure .... and turn on power.

3. When temperature has .... , turn off power.
   Record .... from joulemeter and ....

4. Use your measurements to calculate .... :

$$\text{Specific heat capacity} = \frac{\rule{4cm}{0.4pt}}{\rule{2cm}{0.4pt} \times \text{temperature change}}$$

Investigating Melting Ice

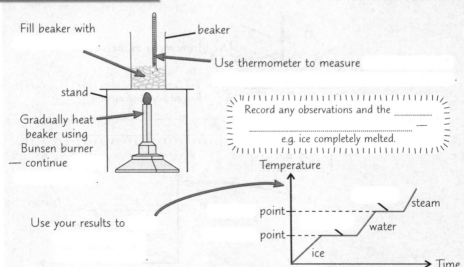

Fill beaker with ....

beaker

Use thermometer to measure ....

stand

Gradually heat beaker using Bunsen burner — continue ....

Record any observations and the ....
.... — ....
e.g. ice completely melted.

Temperature

point ┈┈┈

point ┈┈┈

steam

water

ice

Time

Use your results to ....

Core Practicals

Core Practicals 6

Four Steps to Find the Specific Heat Capacity of Water

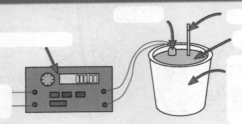

1 Fill the

2 Measure

3 When temperature

4 Use

$$\text{Specific heat capacity} = \frac{\rule{4cm}{0.4pt}}{\rule{1.5cm}{0.4pt} \times \rule{1.5cm}{0.4pt}}$$

Investigating Melting Ice

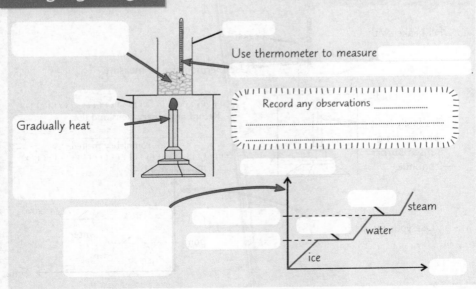

Use thermometer to measure

Record any observations ....

Gradually heat

steam

water

ice

Mixed Practice Quizzes

Blimey, that was a lot of practicals. Here are some quizzes for you on p.139-150.

Quiz 1   Date: ...... / ...... / ......

1) Describe an experiment to measure the speed of a wave in a solid.
2) List the apparatus needed in an experiment to find the density of a liquid.
3) What shape is the *I-V* graph for a filament lamp?
4) Describe an experiment you could do to investigate how well different materials emit radiation.
5) What is the dependent variable in the experiment where hanging masses are added to a spring?
6) Describe an experiment to measure the temperature of ice as it is heated.
7) When using a trolley to test how increasing the force applied affects acceleration, what is the control variable?
8) How can you determine the density of a regular solid?
9) Describe an experiment you could do to investigate refraction.
10) What is the purpose of using thermal insulation when investigating the specific heat capacity of water?

Total:

Quiz 2   Date: ...... / ...... / ......

1) Describe an experiment to find the *I-V* graph for a single resistor.
2) List the apparatus needed for a trolley experiment to test *F = ma*.
3) Name one piece of apparatus that can be used to provide a beam of light.
4) What should you do if a circuit you are investigating begins to heat up?
5) How should the height of the ramp be set when testing *F = ma*?
6) Describe how a pair of light gates can be used to measure acceleration.
7) Which pair of lines do you measure the angle of incidence between?
8) What is the independent variable in the experiment where hanging masses are added to a spring?
9) True or false? When investigating the effect of adding components in parallel, each branch of the circuit should have an ammeter and a voltmeter.
10) Describe an experiment to find the force-extension relationship of a spring.

Total:

Core Practicals

Mixed Practice Quizzes

Quiz 3 Date: ...... / ...... / ......

1) Describe how to use a density bottle to measure the volume of a solid.

2) State the independent, dependent and control variables in the $F = ma$ experiment where masses are added to the trolley, but not the hanging mass.

3) How can you find the work done by a force on a spring from a graph of the force applied to the spring against the extension of the spring?

4) How does p.d. across the components differ in series and parallel circuits?

5) How could you find the frequency of water waves in a ripple tank?

6) What is the wavelength of the loudest sound wave created by striking a rod?

7) How could you measure the extension of a spring?

8) Give two control variables when investigating the emission of radiation by water in test tubes covered with different materials.

9) Describe how to find the specific heat capacity of water.

10) Describe how to measure the speed of water waves in a ripple tank.

Total:

Quiz 4 Date: ...... / ...... / ......

1) What piece of apparatus can be used to measure a trolley's acceleration?

2) What is the dependent variable in the investigation of the emission of radiation by water in test tubes covered with different surfaces?

3) In the experiments to test $F = ma$, what force causes the trolley to move?

4) How do you find the force on a spring being stretched by hanging masses?

5) Describe the shape of the temperature-time graph resulting from heating ice over a period of time.

6) How do you find the average wavelength of water waves in a ripple tank?

7) Give three pieces of apparatus you could use in an experiment to measure the speed of sound waves in air.

8) What two quantities must be found to measure the density of something?

9) Describe how to investigate the relationship between current, p.d. and resistance for a single component.

10) What quantity is measured by a joulemeter?

Total:

Core Practicals

Apparatus and Techniques

First Go:
...../...../.....

Measuring Length

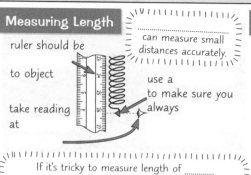

ruler should be

to object

take reading
at

can measure small
distances accurately.

use a
to make sure you
always

If it's tricky to measure length of ....
.... (e.g. ....
of one water wave), measure length of e.g. ....
.... and .... to find length of ....

Measuring the Volume of a Liquid

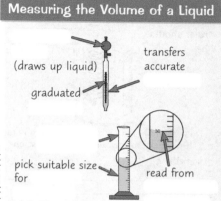

(draws up liquid)

graduated

transfers
accurate

pick suitable size
for

read from

Measuring Angles

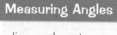

align angle vertex
with

measure the angle

line up

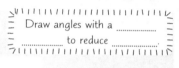

Draw angles with a ....
.... to reduce ....

with one angle line

Safety

safety

If using ...., don't
look directly into them.

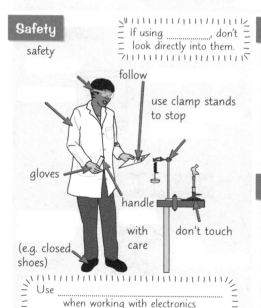

follow

use clamp stands
to stop

gloves

handle

with
care

don't touch

(e.g. closed
shoes)

Use ....
when working with electronics
to prevent ....

Measuring Temperature

wait for

to stabilise

bulb fully

read off
scale at

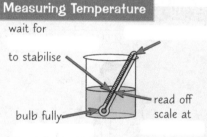

Measuring Mass

liquid or solid to

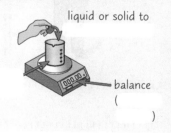

balance
(
)

Apparatus and Techniques

Measuring Length

ruler should be

Micrometers ....
....
....

use a

If it's tricky to measure length of just one of something ....
....
....
....

Measuring Angles

align angle

measure

Safety

If using ....
....

use

handle

Measuring the Volume of a Liquid

transfers

graduated pipette

pick suitable

Draw angles ....
....

Measuring Temperature

wait for

Measuring Mass

liquid

empty container

Practical Skills

Working with Electronics

Voltmeters

Connect a voltmeter
with a device to measure the
.... across it.

Ammeters

Connect an ammeter
with a device to measure
the current ....

Make sure you use an ammeter or voltmeter with
an ...., e.g. mA, mV.

Multimeters

Multimeters are devices that can
measure ....,
or ....

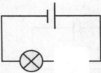

Connect them correctly and turn the
dial to ....

Light Gates

Time can also be measured with ....

Light beam is shone from
....
to ....

.... to computer.
Computer measures time that light
beam is ....

Two quantities measured using light gates:

1 Speed

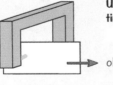

object passes through

Use .... and
time that light beam is broken to
....

2 Acceleration

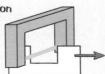

shape of object means

Calculate speed of
.... and use this to
calculate ....

156

Working with Electronics

Voltmeters

Connect a voltmeter

Ammeters

Connect an ammeter

Make sure you _____
_____.

Multimeters

Multimeters are devices

Connect

Light Gates

Light beam

Detector

Two quantities measured using light gates:

1 Speed

object

2 _____

Calculate speed

Mixed Practice Quizzes

Final question time, don't be too sad. These delightful quiz questions test the content from pages 153-156. You know the drill by now — get cracking.

Quiz 1 — Date: ...... / ...... / ......

1) True or false? An ammeter should be connected in parallel with a device to measure the current through it.

2) What can be used to draw liquid up into a pipette?

3) What is a multimeter?

4) Describe what you could do to measure the wavelength of a water wave if you were finding it hard to directly measure one with a ruler.

5) Give two quantities that can be measured using a light gate.

6) Why should a clamp stand be used when suspending masses from a spring?

7) What characteristic of a measuring cylinder must you consider before an experiment, and why?

8) Give two things you must do when measuring the length of an object.

9) Name the apparatus used for measuring the angle between two lines.

10) True or false? You should take a thermometer reading at eye level.

Total:

Quiz 2 — Date: ...... / ...... / ......

1) Give one safety precaution you should follow when working with lasers.

2) How does a light gate work?

3) What value should a mass balance be set to before measuring mass?

4) When measuring the length of an object, what could a marker be used for?

5) Give two ways of measuring the volume of a liquid.

6) True or false? A voltmeter should be connected in parallel with a device to measure the potential difference across it.

7) True or false? Using electronics at a low voltage causes overheating.

8) An object passes through a light gate. What two quantities are needed to calculate the speed of the object?

9) How should you use a protractor to measure an angle?

10) What apparatus can be used to accurately measure small distances?

Total:

Practical Skills

Mixed Practice Quizzes

Quiz 3   Date: ...... / ...... / ......

1) What device is capable of measuring either current or potential difference?
2) What is a micrometer used for?
3) Give one piece of apparatus that can measure time.
4) Why should you use a sharp pencil when drawing angles?
5) Which part of a protractor should you align the angle vertex with?
6) What is a light gate connected to?
7) What apparatus could you use to transfer an accurate volume of liquid?
8) Give four possible safety precautions you could take during an experiment.
9) How should you connect an ammeter to measure the current of a device?
10) Describe how to use a light gate to measure the acceleration of an object.

Total:

Quiz 4   Date: ...... / ...... / ......

1) True or false? You should measure the temperature reading on a thermometer as soon as the bulb is fully submerged in a liquid.
2) Name a device that can be used to measure resistance.
3) What is a graduated pipette used for?
4) What is a protractor used for?
5) Which part of the meniscus should readings be taken from when measuring volume?
6) How should you connect a voltmeter to measure the voltage of a device?
7) How many times does an object need to interrupt the light beam of a light gate to measure its acceleration?
8) When using a ruler, what can you use to make sure you always measure length from the same point?
9) Name two safety items that can be worn whilst performing an experiment.
10) True or false? A ruler should be perpendicular to an object when measuring its length.

Total: